THE INDIANA SAND DUNES AND SHORE LINES OF THE LAKE MICHIGAN BASIN

THE UNIVERSITY OF CHICAGO PRESS
CHICAGO, ILLINOIS

—

THE BAKER & TAYLOR COMPANY
NEW YORK

THE MACMILLAN COMPANY OF CANADA, LIMITED
TORONTO

THE CAMBRIDGE UNIVERSITY PRESS
LONDON

THE MARUZEN-KABUSHIKI-KAISHA
TOKYO, OSAKA, KYOTO, FUKUOKA, SENDAI

THE COMMERCIAL PRESS, LIMITED
SHANGHAI

THE GEOGRAPHIC SOCIETY OF CHICAGO
BULLETIN No. 8

THE INDIANA SAND DUNES AND SHORE LINES OF THE LAKE MICHIGAN BASIN

By

GEORGE BABCOCK CRESSEY

PUBLISHED FOR THE GEOGRAPHIC SOCIETY OF CHICAGO

By

THE UNIVERSITY OF CHICAGO PRESS
CHICAGO, ILLINOIS

Composed and Printed By
The University of Chicago Press
Chicago, Illinois, U.S.A.

PREFACE

The southern and eastern shores of Lake Michigan are fringed by a remarkable belt of sand dunes. Although dunes are common features of deserts and sea coasts, it is only under exceptional conditions that they reach the development shown in this area. This paper deals with those items which are of geographic or geologic interest and is largely a discussion of the principles of eolian activity and the evolution of the Indiana portion of Lake Michigan since the retreat of the last ice sheet. The object is to explain the origin of the dunes rather than to describe the many beautiful areas which exist in the region.

While the scope of this work is largely geological, it would be unfair to those readers who may be unfamiliar with the region not to mention some of its other points of interest.

Due to the location at the head of the lake, all travel between the east and the northwest must pass through or near the area, and many romantic events of the early days are associated with it. Father Marquette and Chevalier de LaSalle both passed along the shore of the lake, while later the stage route between Detroit and Chicago led through the dune country, partly along the beach and in part through the dunes. At this time a fort and two or more taverns, which had their full share of frontier romance, existed among the dunes. In the early part of the nineteenth century there was a logging town at Waverly Beach with a reported population of 1,500, while "City West," near Tremont, was at one time larger than Chicago. When the early settlers came, from 1825 to 1830, the land was occupied by the Pottawatomie Indians who were friendly to the newcomers. The first settlers were principally from the Atlantic states and were generally well educated and thrifty, so that prosperous communities rapidly developed. Within recent years the industrial districts in the western part of the area have brought a great increase in the population.

The dune country likewise holds great interest because of its rich assemblage of plant and animal life. Many species not found elsewhere for many miles are abundant in the dunes, while the various environments of shifting sands and tamarack swamps furnish splendid examples of ecological relationships. During the summer months the dunes furnish a popular vacation area and thousands of people take advantage of the many beauty spots and the wonderful bathing beaches (Plate III, *a*).

In view of this widespread interest in the dunes as a recreation center,

Indiana has set off a portion of the area as a state park, and it is greatly to be hoped that much more of the region may soon be preserved in some such form.

Despite the significance of the area, relatively little study has been devoted to its geology. The bibliography (chap. vi) lists the chief references, and attention is directed especially to the soil surveys of Porter and Lake counties and to the work of Blatchley in 1897. For the historical geology of the region the writer has drawn much from the writings of Leverett and Baker. The field work on which this *Bulletin* is based was carried on during 1920, 1921, and 1923. The area studied is a little over 200 square miles in extent and includes 150 miles of shore lines of the former glacial lakes.

Acknowledgments are gratefully made to the many who have aided in the work. First of all should be mentioned the late Professor Rollin D. Salisbury, at whose suggestion the problem was undertaken and to whose interest and guidance the report owes much of any value which it may possess. The author is also under obligation to Professor J H. Bretz for aid in the final preparation of the report. Many others have furnished help and suggestions, but it is impossible to name them all. The author especially desires to express his appreciation to those who have placed their photographs at his disposal, and it is only to be regretted that it is impossible to use more of the 1,000 which were examined. The railroads which pass through the area have been generous in supplying profiles of their roads, thus furnishing almost the only available records of elevations for the former beach lines. During the summer of 1922 the writer held an appointment as field assistant under the Indiana Department of Geology, and this proved to be of considerable help in the prosecution of the work. Finally, the writer is under deep indebtedness to the Geographic Society of Chicago in connection with the publication of the *Bulletin*.

This study was accepted by the faculty of the Ogden Graduate School of Science of the University of Chicago as a dissertation for the degree of Doctor of Philosophy in the Department of Geology.

TABLE OF CONTENTS

vii

LIST OF ILLUSTRATIONS

[1] Plates II–XX follow p. 77.

CHAPTER I

GENERAL GEOGRAPHY

LOCATION

The sand dunes of Lake Michigan are largely confined to the southern and eastern shores, though a few small dunes are found along the Wisconsin shore. This survey is confined almost entirely to the Indiana dunes, except in so far as the source of the sand lies outside. Many of the Michigan dunes rise higher above the lake than those of Indiana, but they are commonly built upon glacial drift which itself is higher than the lake, and their altitude therefore is not a measure of the height of the dunes. Furthermore, the Michigan belt of dunes is narrower than the dune sand area in Indiana.

That part of Indiana which is involved extends from the Illinois to the Michigan boundaries and as far south of the present shore line as the highest beach of the glacial lakes (see map). This southern limit is the inner margin of the Valparaiso Moraine which curves around the lake concentrically. The area lies within Lake, Porter, and La Porte counties and is 39 miles from east to west and 19 miles from north to south. There are other dunes in northern Indiana formed in association with glacial lakes in the Kankakee River Valley, but the term "sand dunes of northwestern Indiana" as used in this paper refers only to those associated with the Lake Michigan basin.

CLIMATE

The most significant climatic element in dune growth is that of wind. The winds largely control the lake currents and the character of the waves, together with the resulting along-shore drift, and in the formation and re-shaping of dunes the wind is of outstanding importance. Data relative to the direction and velocities of the winds are thus fundamental. No wind records for northern Indiana are available from the weather bureau, the nearest station being at the University of Chicago, thirty miles distant from the dune country. The relation of these records to conditions within the dune area is uncertain. The directions are doubtless quite similar, but the velocities are subject to considerable correction, since the University observatory is located a mile west of the lake and all winds there recorded have been checked by buildings. The dune country has an average shore line direction of N. 60° E., and, since all winds from the level surface of the lake tend to be stronger, the winds from northerly points, between west and northeast, presumably have higher velocities than those listed in the records of the weather bureau.

While the winds of the dune country come from all quarters of the compass, those with a westerly component are the most significant. Since most of the district is covered with vegetation and only along the shore are there extensive areas of shifting sand, the most effective winds in dune construction and migration are from the lake.

As defined by the weather bureau, winds having velocities in excess of 40 miles per hour are termed gales. These are of large importance in the dunes, since one day of gale may result in greater changes than several months of normal breezes. The surface velocity of the wind during a gale is sufficient to pick up and carry sand in suspension and thus to erode rapidly, whereas with the average velocities but very little movement of sand occurs. In addition to its direct transportation of sand, wind is the dominant factor in the formation of waves and currents which are of very great importance in supplying sand for the Indiana dunes.

The rainfall of the dune country averages 33 inches per year, every month having at least 2 inches, and the maximum occurring in the spring. The area thus receives abundant moisture for a diversified vegetation. The sand is too coarse to permit capillary attraction to bring moisture to the surface for evaporation, and much of the water is thus retained in the sand and is available for the vegetation. At all times there is moist sand at a depth of a few inches in almost any location. Following a rain the surface dries rapidly and the wind may speedily again become operative.

Because of the low temperatures during the winter months, the surface of the dunes is often frozen and thus stabilized. A blanket of snow is likewise effective in protecting the sand from the wind.

PHYSIOGRAPHY

GENERAL

The topography of the dune country may be traced directly to the lacustrine and eolian processes which have been operative since the retreat of the Wisconsin ice sheet. The Valparaiso Moraine, immediately south of the area, is a strongly marked recessional moraine belt which is concentric about the southern end of Lake Michigan. When the area to the north of this moraine was exposed by the receding ice front it was inclosed on the south by the moraine and on the north by the ice sheet, and a series of glacial lakes came into existence, with various elevations due to changing outlets. Thus a series of beach lines was formed and in association with each was developed a belt of dunes.

The general physiography of the area consists of two types: (1) the complex irregular topography of the dune belts along the present and the earlier shore lines, and (2) the intervening flat areas between the beaches, often occupied by marshes. The main dune complex along Lake Michigan is the outstanding feature (Plate II). It averages a mile in width and, except for the areas of shifting sand near the shore, is almost entirely forested. These areas of shifting sand project inland from the lake into the wooded tract as great tongues of sand and are commonly free from vegetation. Within the dune belt the very uneven topography consists of the hills, short ridges, and basins which are characteristic of dune tracts. Some of the slopes are as steep as 32°, the angle of rest for loose sand, and the ridges appear at first to have no prevailing orientation. Irregular hollows often lie within the complex. The relief within small areas in many places is 100 feet, while the maximum is twice that figure. The topography is almost entirely due to eolian activity, there having been very little reshaping subsequent to the formation of the dunes. In the belts of dunes on the old shore lines the relief is less and the slopes are more gentle.

The level tracts separating the dune belts are typically marsh or muck land. There is almost no relief, and where undrained or uncultivated, these level tracts are covered with grasses or swamp vegetation. In part these belts are now lakes or the low flood plains of streams (Plate III, *b*).

The dune areas are largely uninhabited except for summer residents along the lake (Plate III, *a*). Locally the flat intervening belts between the shore lines have been drained and are devoted to farming, but the population is scattered. Toward the Illinois border the Calumet industrial region has taken over much of the land, especially around the cities of Gary, Indiana Harbor, Hammond, and Whiting, and the cultural development has quite altered the landscape. The same is true to a less degree at Michigan City, which is the oldest city in the region.

THE PRESENT SHORE LINE

The present shore line of southern Lake Michigan is remarkably regular and, within the principal region of dune development, from Gary to Michigan City, it is almost straight, having a trend of N. 60° E. Nowhere on the southern boundary of the lake are there any promontories or deep embayments. During the earlier lake stages such features must have been conspicuous, but by the work of the shore processes a regular coast line has now been developed. While the general trend of the shore is smooth, small irregularities are common. Crescentic embayments, the points of which are known as beach cusps, are conspicuous (Plate IV, *a*). From tip to tip the cusps range from 5 feet to 200 feet, and the projections may extend as much as 15 feet into the lake.

West of Gary the construction of railroads and the industrial developments along the shore have narrowed and almost obscured the beach. At Miller the beach averages about 350 feet in width, and it is progressively narrower to the east (Plate IV, *b*). At Dune Park it is 250 feet wide; at Waverly, 200 feet; at Johnsville, 100 feet; at Long Beach, 75 feet. These figures vary greatly from year to year according to the storms and currents, but are representative. The beach is sandy with almost no shells and relatively few pebbles. The small quantity of beach shingle varies from place to place and from time to time, but it is rarely sufficient to cover the sand. The beach shingle is composed almost entirely of flat pebbles of a greenish drab, fine-grained sandstone, which resembles a shale. Presumably this is from the Antrim shale (of Devonian age) which underlies the glacial drift in this area. Fragments of igneous rock are not abundant, but there is frequently a considerable amount of scoriaceous slag from the steel mills to the west.

Both the southeastern shore within the state of Michigan and the western shore north of Chicago are being eroded. A wave-cut cliff of glacial till extends north of Chicago to Waukegan (Plate V, *a*). In many places it is more than 75 feet high, and the beach accompanying it is quite narrow. In Michigan erosion is also in progress, although the till is usually masked with sand (Plate V, *b*). The material derived from these cliffs is transported by waves and currents along the shore to the head of the lake where it is deposited, and thus the beach is widened.

THE MAIN DUNE COMPLEX

The term "dune complex" is here employed for the belt of dunes along the Indiana shore of Lake Michigan (Plate II). This belt extends inland more or less continuously to a strip of flat, marshy land which marks its landward limit. Though most of the dunes of the belt do not antedate the present stage of the lake, yet it includes dunes which are related to higher lake levels. The belt ranges in width from a mile and a quarter at Miller to half a mile or less at Michigan City. In view of the extreme irregularity of the topography and the manner in which the individual dune units have interacted and become mixed, the term "complex" seems appropriate.

There are no high dunes in the belt west of Gary; instead, there are many small parallel ridges, in part dunelets but largely of subaqueous origin. These ridges are from 5 to 12 feet high and average 150 feet in width. Both the ridges and the depressions are strikingly regular. The most remarkable feature is the linear arrangement, many of the ridges and swales continuing for several miles roughly parallel to the present shore without change in character. In many localities these features have been obscured by the industrial development, but they formerly extended north through the City of Chicago. The Bureau of Soils Map of Lake County shows seventy of these ridges east of Hammond. Scrub oaks grow on these ridges, while a swamp flora is found in the depressions. Many of the swales contain standing water.

The real dune complex commences immediately east of Gary and is well developed north of Miller. Here the beach is wide and the dunes are actively growing. The landward side of the beach grades up into the low dunes, where the movement of the sand is partially arrested by grasses. Generally there is next to the beach a ridge known as the fore dune, which, near Miller, reaches a height of approximately 40 feet. Where this is not a continuous ridge it is represented by a line of more or less connected hills. This is the area of cottonwood trees and the sand is only partially fixed. Farther inland the cover of vegetation is progressively greater, and in succession occur the region of oaks and the region of pines. The latter are found where there is no shifting sand and where the slopes are more gentle. The dune country offers many splendid examples of the control of vegetation by environment.

Between the former mouth of the Grand Calumet River and Gary not more than 25 per cent of the dune area north of the river is covered with vegetation. The sand is thus exposed to the wind and changes are continually in progress. There are numerous basins inclosed by the advance of dunes from different directions and possibly in part due to wind scour. The relief does not exceed 60 feet. South of the river and extending nearly a mile from the lake, the dunes are entirely forested and there is no shifting sand. The hills are lower than to the north and the slopes are less steep.

East of the former mouth of the Grand Calumet River the shore phase is similar to that farther west, but in place of the abrupt contrast found between the north and south banks of the river, there is a gradation both physiographically and ecologically. The fore dune, or ridge immediately along the beach, is well developed and the transition to the stable dunes of the interior is gradual. Several ridges and isolated hills reach 100 feet in height and there are many small lakelets and marshy ponds. Nowhere else in the dune complex are there so many of these little bodies of water;

within two square miles there are at least two dozen. Commonly these depressions have steep northern sides. These ponds are best developed among the dunes about half a mile south of the lake, and between them and the rather high fore dune is a fairly continuous belt of marsh parallel to the shore.

Some of the most striking features of the dune complex are the elongated areas of nearly bare sand which project, tonguelike, inland from the shore. These are known as "blowouts" and are amphitheater-like excavations in the dune sand accumulation, open toward the lake (Plate III, *a*). They have been formed by wind erosion and consequent movement of the sand landward. Their slope toward the beach is from 2° to 3°, while the landward slope is almost everywhere 32°, the angle of rest for the loose dry sand of the dunes. On a small scale these are present in the shifting sands east of Miller Beach, but they are typically produced only where most of the dune ridge is held by vegetation. Between Miller Beach and the beach north of Wicliffe they are conspicuously developed and vary in length from a few tens of feet to several hundreds. At Wicliffe Beach is a large blowout which reaches back a quarter of a mile into the dunes; much of its lower portion near the shore has of recent years been filling up. Farther east the blowouts are more conspicuous.

At Dune Park there is a tract of nearly a square mile from which the dunes have been removed, the sand having been used for commercial purposes in Chicago. This tract was formerly the site of the largest blowout in the area and thus furnished a great amount of loose sand easily accessible for steam-shovel excavation. The western part of this cleared region has been covered subsequently by shifting sands and somewhat resembles the shore east of Miller Beach; most of the area, however, is relatively flat. The dune complex is here about a mile wide.

East of Dune Park the beach narrows somewhat and the character of the shore face changes. The fore dune is small and poorly developed and the higher dunes come close to the beach, there being a rather precipitous face which ranges in height from 75 to 125 feet. Blowouts are numerous, there being eight in the six miles between Dune Park and Waverly Beach. The zone of cottonwoods is narrower and the oaks come up to the edge of the shore face. Within the dunes there are many ridges roughly parallel to the shore and a few old blowouts may be seen, now entirely forested and fixed. There are several higher points near the shore whose elevations are greater than 150 feet: Mount Tom, 200 feet; Mount Lehman, 160 feet, and Mount Tuthill, 150 feet, are examples (Plate VI, *a*). At a distance of about half a mile from the beach there is a belt of marsh or level land underlain by a foot or so of muck. This is interrupted by numerous transverse dunes, but the patches of marsh may easily be traced in the field or observed on Goodman's map of the dunes or on the Chicago Geographic Society's map of Dune Park. The dunes immediately to the south of this belt and still within the complex are smoother, and the relief does not commonly exceed 50 feet. This region, including Dune Park and Waverly Beach, is one of the most attractive portions of the dune country and embraces diverse types of topographic forms. Except for the blowouts, it is all covered with vegetation and all but the meadows and marshes are forested. On the blowouts are extensive areas of shifting sand, but elsewhere loose sand is confined to patches a few yards in extent.

Immediately east of Sand Creek, at Waverly Beach, are three high dunes, Mounts Tom, Holden, and Green (Plate VI, *a*). Mount Tom, the highest point in the dunes area, is at least 200 feet above the lake, while the others are 170 feet and 160 feet high.

At Waverly Beach the belt of dunes is about three-fourths of a mile wide, and gradually narrows to the east. The patchy belt of marsh found to the west is largely obscured east of Waverly and the shore face of the dunes is more abrupt, with the fore dune almost entirely absent except across the mouths of larger blowouts which have flatter slopes than the normal shore face and thus afford room for sand accumulation. There are symmetrical blowouts here, but none of them extend as far inland as those to the west. Within the complex the aspect of the dunes is much the same as that already described. Here is Brown's Ridge, a large, well-preserved forested blowout. Where Johnsfield Creek cuts through the dunes the belt is but one-third of a mile wide and erosion by the waves is actively going on along the beach. Between this point and Michigan City wind erosion is so active that new vegetation finds it difficult to secure a foothold. A few blowouts are developed, but in general the shifting winds have produced a confused medley of dune forms which on the landward side are gradually burying the older forested belt under advancing waves of sand.

In the western part of Michigan City there was formerly a blowout dune nearly 200 feet high, called Hoosier Slide by the early settlers. This has now been entirely removed for the making of sand-lime brick and for other commercial purposes. The beach here is but 50 feet wide.

Immediately east of Michigan City there are several high dunes. Due to the construction of breakwaters, the shore is here protected from erosion and the beach is locally 300 feet wide. The dune belt from here on to the Michigan state line does not exceed a quarter of a mile in width and the individual dunes are much lower and more rounded than to the west. Along the beach erosion is rapidly taking place and the shore face is steep. The fore dune is entirely absent. There are no blowouts and there is but little shifting sand. Most of this belt has been laid out in residential subdivisions, so that normal dune processes are no longer operative.

INTERIOR BEACH LINES AND DUNES

To the south of the main dune complex are other narrower belts of dunes, built up along the various beach lines of the glacial lakes which occupied the Lake Michigan basin. These have been reworked in part by the wind and also by man, and almost everywhere the slopes are gentle. The older shore lines are for the most part more irregular than the present one and are diversified with embayments and headlands. The character of the beaches is therefore varied. In part they are marked by shore lines cut into the moraines; in other places there were bays a few feet to a few inches in depth and there was very little cutting or deposition. Bars and spits were therefore developed and accumulation of sand, either subaqueous or subaerial, occurred only where conditions were locally favorable. These localities indicate that the currents and winds for the various earlier stages of the lake apparently were essentially the same as at present.

Where the former beaches are roughly parallel to the present shore and fairly regular, there is a belt of dunes a few hundred yards wide and 10–40 feet high. The old beach itself is well preserved, though the actual line of the water level is rarely recognizable. Pebbles are as rare as on the present beach.

Between each of the beach-and-dune belts there is usually a strip or zone of flat meadow land. Prevailingly the soil is muck and the drainage is usually so poor that the belt is marshy except where artificially drained. From Miller to Michigan City such a strip lies immediately southeast of the main complex and is practically continuous, except near Wicliffe. Farther from the lake the level land between the dune belts is higher, better drained, and more irregular in outline, but is nevertheless topographically distinct from the dune belts. Southeast of Dune Park, in Porter County, there was a large embayment which at the highest stage of water extended east along the Little Calumet River to La Porte County, and south along Salt Creek nearly to the Pennsylvania Railroad. At this stage of the glacial lake there was also an island west of Hobart.

The character of the interior beaches and dunes will be considered in greater detail in the chapter on "Historical Geology."

CHAPTER II

GENERAL GEOLOGY

PREGLACIAL TOPOGRAPHY

Bed rock is nowhere exposed in northern Indiana, and its character and the altitude of its surface are known only from wells. Table I presents the available information.[1]

The uppermost rock formation encountered in all but one of the wells is a dark-colored fine sandstone or shale. The color ranges from brownish to olive green and blue. Its continuation to the northeast has been mapped

TABLE I

Location	Depth to Bed Rock below Surface (Feet)	Elevation of Bed Rock above Sea-Level (Feet)
Hammond...	110	486
Gary (Illinois Steel Company)......................	119	475
Hobart (Owens Brick Yard)........................	150	481
Tremont (Wilson & Company)......................	140	466
N. E. Porter Company (Blair Well, Sec. 1, T. 37 N., R. 5 W.).....	240	361
Michigan City (penitentiary).......................	172	425
Michigan City (gas well)...........................	252	351
Michigan City (penitentiary).......................	235*	....
Michigan City (Sullivan Machinery Company)........	263	....

*Bed rock not reached at this depth.

by the Michigan Geological Survey as the Antrim shale of Devonian age. Little is known of its distribution in northern Indiana, except that it is patchy. Commonly it is thin, but it reaches 76 feet at Michigan City. The lower portion of the drift is commonly filled with fragments of this shale. The well of the Sullivan Machinery Company penetrates 30 feet of Devonian limestone. Below the Antrim lies the Niagara limestone, of Silurian age. Its thickness at East Chicago is 490 feet, and most wells sunk to this horizon supply artesian water which is strongly sulphurous.

GLACIATION

The history of the various Pleistocene ice invasions is interpreted from the record of the glacial drift. Well logs show a succession of sand and

[1] Most of the data are from Leverett, *U.S. Geol. Survey Water Supply Paper 21* (1899), and *U.S. Geol. Survey Monograph 38* (1899), p. 392.

9

clay (till) deposits and, while these have not been correlated in detail for this immediate area, it is probable that northwestern Indiana was over-ridden at least three times by glacial ice. While the basin of Lake Michigan probably was originally a preglacial river valley, the ice did much to scour and deepen this trough. Alternations in the character of the drift penetrated by the wells probably indicate alternate presence of glacial ice and glacial lakes. The drift is commonly rather stoneless in the west, while toward Michigan there is a considerable percentage of gravel.

Several horizons within the drift carry artesian water. The Indiana penitentiary at Michigan City has put down fifteen eight-inch wells which give flows of pure water. The logs for these wells averaged: Sand, 36 feet; blue clay, 48 feet; "hard pan," 1 foot; total, 85 feet. Another well found a very fine sand at 235 feet.

THE LATE WISCONSIN ICE SHEET

The outstanding characteristic of the last ice sheet to invade this region—the Late Wisconsin—was its lobate development. One large lobe occupied the Lake Michigan basin and extended to central Indiana. In its waning stages it built successive recessional moraines which embrace the lake like great letter U's. One of the most strongly marked of these moraines passes through Crown Point and Valparaiso and is known as the Valparaiso Moraine. Its width is approximately 15 miles at the Illinois border and decreases to about 8 miles at the Michigan border, and its elevation above sea-level ranges from 750 feet in Lake County to nearly 900 feet in La Porte County. Its surface is very uneven, with many low knobs and shallow basins, some containing lakelets. Its inner border is rather abrupt and forms the southern boundary of the area considered in this paper.

Following the protracted period when the Valparaiso Moraine was built there came a time when melting exceeded supply and the ice margin retreated northward. In this retreat a series of small recessional moraines was developed, known as the Lake-Border Morainic System. In Illinois and in Michigan there are three ridges. In Lake County, Indiana, the component ridges are largely absent, while in Porter and La Porte counties there are but two present. The outer or southernmost of these two ridges averages a mile and a half wide and is distinctly traceable near the Michigan line about 6 miles east of and parallel to the lake. Where it is crossed by Trail Creek, east of Michigan City, it is very weakly developed. From Trail Creek westward to the vicinity of Furnessville the ridge is double and the members are separated by a marsh a mile or less in width.

From Furnessville to Baileytown it is a single ridge. West of Baileytown it is not identifiable unless the low undulating ridge which extends about 6 miles west of Hobart may mark the continuation of this outer ridge. A north-south moraine ridge extends from a point 2 miles south of Crissman to the Valparaiso Moraine at Wheeler. The exact significance of this ridge is uncertain, but it may represent a turn in the edge of the ice front. It is the middle member of the three ridges in Michigan, known as Covert Ridge, which is very poorly developed in Indiana. It is about a mile from the lake.

Both in Michigan and Wisconsin are moraines, younger than the lake-border system, which continue the recessional history of the ice sheet. The ice retreat was not regular; there were halts of varying duration and even strongly marked readvances of the ice.

GLACIO-LACUSTRINE HISTORY

The plain at the inner border of the Valparaiso Moraine is about 50 feet above Lake Michigan near the Illinois line, and about 70 feet near the Michigan boundary. As the ice front receded northward from the Valparaiso Moraine, a lake was formed between the moraine and the retreating Lake Michigan ice lobe. A detailed description of this lake is presented in chapter vi, "Historical Geology." There are three distinct shore lines at 55 feet, 35 feet, and 20 feet above Lake Michigan. The glacial lake stages recorded by these shore lines are, respectively, the Glenwood, Calumet, and Tolleston-Hammond, and they are related to the larger bodies of water known as Lakes Chicago, Algonquin, and Nipissing. The development of the present Lake Michigan did not consist merely in a lowering of level by the erosion of the Chicago outlet, for there are several intermediate low-water stages when the Chicago outlet must have been dry. These low-water stages were due to large oscillations of the ice front which uncovered lower outlets to the north. Interaction with other of the glacial lakes also caused several changes of level. Tilting movements of the land to the north were likewise a factor. When the ice abandoned the Strait of Mackinac and the St. Lawrence Valley, drainage was free to take its present course and the history of Lake Michigan proper began.

PRESENT CHANGES

The most rapid physiographic changes now in progress are those associated with the dune complex bordering the lake. In the interior the streams are commonly sluggish and erosion is relatively slow, the chief exception being Deep River, which flows in a narrow steep-sided valley. In the dunes most of the hills are forested and it is only along the shore or

where sand is exposed to the wind that change is rapid. Around the head
of the lake deposition by littoral currents is widening the beach and new
dune ridges are being constructed; to the east, however, the waves are
eroding the beach and in places the storm waves cut back the foot of the
dunes, thus making a destructional rather than a constructional coast.
Here the lakeward face of the dunes is abrupt, and the more mature topography and vegetation of the older dunes is close to the beach.

Wherever the protective covering of vegetation is removed in exposed
situations, the wind rapidly scours a "channel" leading back from the
lake. Such "channels" may grow into the amphitheater-like blowouts already described. These blowouts have a certain maximum size beyond
which the wind cannot effectively carry the sand up the long windward
slope. Whenever the wind thus ceases to be dominant, vegetation springs
up and anchors the existing shapes. When blowouts reach such a size that
their surface near the beach is nearly level, new dune ridges are formed
which may migrate landward and thus tend to fill up the concavity. Active blowouts are only associated with the present beach, but smaller areas
of shifting sands facing all points of the compass are present where winds
are especially effective, as for example on the southern edge of the main
complex overlooking the broad flat to the south, and on the higher hills.

CHAPTER III

SOURCES, TRANSPORTATION, AND ACCUMULATION OF THE SAND

EROSION ON THE EASTERN AND WESTERN SHORES

SOURCES OF MATERIAL

The material of the dunes was gathered by the waves from parts of the shore north of its present position and gradually shifted southward by waves and currents. The gathering grounds were both the eastern and western shores of the lake and the gathering process may still be seen in operation. On the west shore of the lake, bluffs cut in glacial till are well developed north of Chicago and wave-cutting may be seen on the eastern shore north of Michigan City (Plate V, *a* and *b*).

EXTENT OF SHORE EROSION

Along the western shore of the lake the bluff cut by the waves is continuous from the northern limits of Chicago to Waukegan, but there dies out. It is a low bluff in Evanston, but becomes progressively higher northward, having elevations above the lake, at Wilmette, of 30 feet; at Winnetka, 50 feet; at Lakeside, 70 feet; at Glencoe, 80 feet; at Highland Park, 90 feet; at Fort Sheridan, 100 feet; at Lake Forest, 80 feet; at Waukegan, 60 feet.[1]

North of Kenosha a bluff records former wave-cutting, but at present the waves are depositing rather than cutting and a sand flat is being built in front of the bluff.

Slumping is a conspicuous feature of most of the bluffs and indicates that wave erosion is still in progress. From Evanston to Waukegan the beach is commonly less than 75 feet wide, and the face of the bluff is steep. Storm waves cut at the base of the cliff and slumping is shown both by fallen masses of earth and by the lakeward tilt of the trees. In all cases the face of the bluff is fresh and such vegetation as is present started largely on the upper surface and is now sliding downward.

The distance that the shore has receded under the attack of the waves may be inferred approximately from the slope of the surfaces that crown

---

[1] These figures refer to the bluff proper; in many cases 10–20 feet should be added to obtain the maximum cutting where stream erosion has lowered the upper surface.

the bluffs. Back from the top of the bluffs the surface slopes gently toward the lake. The intersection of the lakeward projection of this gentle slope with the lake surface should mark roughly the position of the shore line before wave-cutting began. No estimates of this sort were made by the writer, but a number of estimates by others may be mentioned as roughly indicative of the rate and distance of shore retreat. Based largely on surveys and covering periods of from 10 to 35 years, Andrews[1] derives the following figures for the coast from Manitowoc to Evanston, a distance of 180 miles. North of Milwaukee the average rate of cliff retreat was 4.33 feet per year; and to the south, 6.24 feet per year; the average being 5.28 feet. Soundings indicate a rather definite subaqueous terrace all around the lake at a maximum depth of 60 feet, the probable limit of effective wave action. Along the west coast this is from 2 to 6 miles wide, averaging 3.98 miles. This terrace is formed partly by wave-cutting and partly by deposition; Andrews places the average position of the original shore line as 2.72 miles lakeward. Later work by the Wisconsin Geological Survey[2] gives a lower figure. They found that the most rapid encroachment in Wisconsin was around Racine, where eighteen locations gave an average for the county of 3.33 feet per year. This is quite variable, however, for Professor T. C. Chamberlin found an average erosion during 24 years of 9.73 feet per year at Racine.

The rate of cutting is rapid enough to threaten a number of fine homes near the bluffs, and the construction of breakwaters or groins at right angles to the shore has been resorted to for protection.

Along the eastern shore of the lake less attention has been given to the extent of the encroachment of the lake on the land. Unlike the west coast, sand dunes are present and form an almost continuous strip along the inner margin of the beach; but these dunes in part are merely a veneer upon drift which comes above the lake level (Plate VI, *b*). Since some of the dunes reach 200 feet above the lake and face it in abrupt erosional slopes, it is evident that they date back to shore conditions which were more favorable to sand accumulation. In part they represent dunes formed during the earlier and higher stages of the lake; but largely they were formed when the lake was at its present level but the shore was farther west. A very considerable amount of cutting is probable, comparable to that of the west shore.

---

[1] Edmund Andrews, "The North American Lakes Considered as Chronometers of Post-Glacial Time," *Trans. Chicago Academy of Science*, II (1870), 1–24.

[2] *Wisconsin Geological Survey*, II (1877), 231.

TRANSPORTATION

LAKE CURRENTS

The nature and direction of the lake currents have been the subject of considerable controversy. The earliest work was that of Andrews and was based largely on studies of accumulation of sand at breakwaters and of the prevailing winds. Within the area of this report he mapped two currents along the shore, moving to the south on both eastern and western shores and joining at the head of the lake where the combined flow turned northeastward out into the lake. In 1895 Harrington, of the weather bureau, set afloat several hundred bottles, and on the basis of their recovery prepared current charts. He agrees with Andrews that there is a southward-moving current along the western shore; but in place of a separate southward-moving current along the east shore, he continues the western current around the head of the lake and maps it as moving northward along the eastern shore. In the east only two of his bottles uphold Andrews' charting, and while he admits the accumulation of débris along the northern side of Michigan piers, he attributes this to occasional storms. No comprehensive mapping has since been done. It seems evident that on the east shore there is a general northward movement, as Harrington outlined, but that it is a few miles off shore. Close to the east shore, however, according to lake captains, there is a definite southward movement of the water.[1] The cause of these currents is undoubtedly complex; winds, barometric fluctuations, the rotation of the earth, and the small tides all doubtless have a part. Since the winds are so variable, however, the currents are never strong and are often reversed.

EVIDENCES OF SAND MOVEMENT

Whatever may be the nature and character of the currents themselves, it is certain that so far as transportation of the sand is concerned, there is an effectual shifting to the south on both eastern and western shores. The evidence for this is definite. Reference has already been made to the large number of short piers or groins constructed between Evanston and Waukegan to check the cutting by the waves. These breakwaters commonly extend about a hundred feet out into the lake from the beach and are spaced a hundred or more yards apart. Immediately north of each one there is an accumulation of sand which makes the beach much wider than it is immediately south of the obstruction, often two or three times the width. The larger the breakwater, the more extensive is the accumula-

---

[1] Personal communication from Captain C. R. Thayer.

tion (Plate V, *a*). While fewer such piers have been constructed along the east coast, the evidence of southward movement of sand is similar. At both St. Joseph and Michigan City extensive accumulation of sand has taken place on the northeastern side of piers, whereas the beach is of the normal width on the southwestern side of these obstructions. The same is also true of the smaller fishing piers between these two cities.

NATURE OF THE LITTORAL DRIFT

The mechanism of the along-shore transport of sediment is readily understood. When a wave breaks, the up-rushing water on the beach carries with it a certain amount of sand and gravel. When this water loses its momentum, it reaches the limit of advance and there is a momentary halt. Then the backwash occurs and the water and its sand load flow down the beach and back into the lake. If waves strike the shore exactly at right angles, the beach material is moved back and forth over the same route and there is no lateral shifting of the sediment. Because of winds and currents, however, most waves strike the shore obliquely. When such oblique waves break, the up-rush is at an obtuse angle to the shore. When the limit of advance is reached, the backwash is largely if not wholly controlled by gravity and the water flows directly back to the lake with little or no lateral component. Thus under the action of oblique waves, the beach detritus is moved up and along the beach by the up-rush and then directly down the beach by the backwash. By the continuation of this zigzag, to-and-fro shifting, the sand and beach shingle travel along the beach. This process is known as the along-shore or littoral drift. Where a pier or breakwater blocks this along-shore movement, the beach detritus accumulates.

In addition to this transportation of material on or near the beach, much sand is also shifted below the water by the drag of the waves and undertow.

DEFLECTION OF STREAMS

Additional evidence as to the direction of sand transportation is found in the deflection of streams entering the lake. Wherever this littoral movement is in progress, sand accumulates as spits and bars on the side of the stream from which the drift is coming and the stream is deflected in the direction toward which the along-shore current is moving. On the west coast the Chicago River offers the best example of deflection. Prior to the extension of the piers at its mouth in 1830, it was deflected southward and flowed parallel with Michigan Boulevard as far as Madison Street, a distance of nearly half a mile. Another striking instance is the deflection of the former mouth of the Grand Calumet River north of Miller. The deflection in this case was more than 20 miles. In Michigan the beach is narrow and the dunes rise abruptly at its inner margin. No stream deflection on a large scale is known, but two creeks which enter the lake, one north of Johnsfield, 2 miles west of Michigan City, and the other at Waverly Beach, are turned to the west for some distance parallel to the shore. In 1922–23 the deflection averaged 275 feet at Johnsfield Creek, and 450 feet at Waverly.

The southern limit of effective action of the east-shore and west-shore currents varies with changing conditions. In general they become ineffective somewhere between Waverly and Miller Beach. South of a line between the Indiana-Michigan boundary and Chicago, the current from the east is eroding while the current from the west is depositing. Fragments of slag from the Gary Steel Mills indicate that the current of the western shore occasionally reaches almost to Michigan City.

CHANGES OF MATERIAL IN TRANSIT

As the original material of the drift is worked over by the waves and transported southward, distinct changes take place in it. The beach sand and gravel at the foot of the till bluffs that are its source are fairly free from clay, for the latter is carried in suspension out into the lake. Large stones are rather rare, but there is commonly a considerable proportion of coarse gravel known as the beach shingle and composed of fragments of crystalline and sedimentary rocks. These gravel pebbles are usually subangular, and even the finer particles, such as sand, are sharp cornered. With wear by the waves, the fragments of all sizes tend to become rounded. Further data will be presented on this point in chapter v. Another effect of wear in littoral transportation is noted in the composition of the material. The drift is composed of a great variety of minerals, largely unweathered in the lower portions and of varying degrees of hardness, cleavability, and chemical inertness. When exposed to the work of the waves pebbles and sand grains of less resistant minerals are rapidly abraded or decomposed, and a few miles beyond the southernmost drift exposure they largely disappear. The net result of the transportation process on both the eastern and western sides of the lake is that the final product which reaches the dune country, especially between Michigan City and the Indiana-Illinois boundary, is very largely a quartz sand. Few pebbles survive in the transport and minerals other than quartz in the sand seldom total over 5 per cent.

SUBAQUEOUS ACCUMULATION AT THE HEAD OF THE LAKE

As has been outlined previously, the process of sand transportation by the along-shore currents is largely but not wholly confined to the beach. The lakeward limit of sand transport is set by the depth of water in which the larger storm waves agitate the bottom. This depth is approximately 60 feet; and while sand at this depth is moved only during storms, there is a very considerable body of sand shoreward which is in process of being slowly transported. Thus the total bulk of sand in transit is divided between that being actively shifted by the littoral drift and the much larger reservoir of more slowly moving sand under water.

Charts of the United States Lake Survey show that the 60-foot contour roughly defines the limits between sand and clay bottom. Patches of each occur on both sides of this line and the boundary is of course a gradational one. Measured at right angles to the shore the 60-foot or 10-fathom contour has the following distances from land: Benton Harbor and St. Joseph, 3 miles; Michigan City, 5 miles; Waverly Beach, 6½ miles; Miller, 9 miles; Indiana Harbor, 10½ miles; Chicago, 10 miles; Evanston, 6 miles; Waukegan, 3 miles. The thickness of the subaqueous sand deposit increases near shore and also shows a general increase to the south; along the eastern coast no figures are known, but around Chicago the sand averages 15 feet thick. At the head of the lake, opposite the dunes, the sand is 25 feet thick or more near the beach; and at a distance of 1,500 or 2,000 feet offshore, averages 15 feet, being more near Miller and somewhat less to the east. Large quantities of sand have been removed for commercial purposes by sand dredges, and Captain C. R. Thayer[1] reports that in the lower part of the deposit the sand is coarser and that the distribution is patchy and the character of the sand variable. The soundings of the Lake Survey show many shoals and submerged bars, largely of gravel, especially off Indiana Harbor and South Chicago. This subaqueous accumulation of sand and gravel is the natural consequence of the southward movement of material on both sides of the lake.

Where the littoral currents cease to be effective, accumulation therefore takes place; and from this large subaqueous reserve, sand is carried to the beach where it becomes available for the construction of the dunes.

SUBAERIAL ACCUMULATION

BEACH CONSTRUCTION

The source of the sand and its transportation to the head of the lake has been described. The mode of sand accumulation on the beach where

[1] Personal communication.

the continually replenished supply furnishes material for transportation by the wind will next be discussed. As the on-rush of a wave carries water up the beach a certain amount of the water sinks into the sand. This is especially noticeable at the extreme upper limit, where a shiny film may be seen for an instant, after which the sand becomes dull. The back-rush of the wave is therefore less in volume and it starts from a point farther down the beach than the maximum reach of the wave; as a result its velocity and momentum are slightly less than that of the up-rush. In terms of sand transportation this means that the wave carries more material up the beach than it can bring back to the lake. The net result is that the beach is widened and increased in volume. In addition to sand and gravel, the onrush of the wave carries bits of flotsam and jetsam. These fragments are carried on the crest of the advancing flood and strand at the maximum point of advance, resulting in the slight ridges known as wave marks. These ridges are composed of bits of shell and wood and sand and, especially in the western part of Indiana, of a scoriaceous slag from the steel mills of Gary and Indiana Harbor.

Upon exposure to the air the sand becomes the prey of the wind, and with favorable winds may be blown up into the dunes. Normally the sand must be dry before the wind is operative, but with high winds even wet sand is blown about. In the construction of the beach both wind and water are thus factors, and the width of the beach is dependent upon the co-operation of both. Many times the wind blows off shore and sand is carried back into the lake. Storm waves likewise cut back the beach and erode the work of months of slow deposition. This process of transfer from subaerial action on the beach to subaqueous control and vice versa is operative not alone in the dune country but throughout the whole journey of the sand from the bluffs southward. The final product is thus the result of diverse and complex phenomena with many reversals. The net result is the accumulation of sand at the head of the lake where prevailing wind conditions are such as to blow it inland and shape it into dunes. North of Chicago erosion rather than deposition is in progress and the winds also are unfavorable to dune accumulation. In the east erosion is also active; but the west winds are dominant, so that there is a narrow belt of dunes. The greatest bulk of dune sand is around the head of the lake, chiefly between Gary and Michigan City.

SINGING SAND

One of the peculiar phenomena present along the beach is an area of sand which emits a singing or resinous tone when disturbed by the "scuffling" of the feet or by a stick being dragged over the sand. The note is clear and can easily be heard at a distance of 25 feet. The area of this singing sand is between 25 and 100 feet wide and lies parallel to the shore along the lower beach. In walking across the belt even the casual observer is struck by the abrupt boundaries, for the characteristic disappears within a few feet along both the landward and the lakeward side. The sound may be produced at any season of the year when the sand is dry.

Sands producing such sounds have been known in various parts of the world for a thousand years, but are relatively uncommon. Various explanations for this phenomenon have been suggested, all of them inconclusive. Mechanical analyses by the writer show the singing sand to be of the same size and degree of rounding as that of the beach on both sides. Since the wind moves the sand about, the belt of singing sand may one day be composed of grains blown from the dunes and the next of sand washed up by high waves. Thus neither size nor degree of roundness can be the causal factor.

Two other possible causes appear: (1) the formation by evaporation of a film of salts about each grain, and (2) a certain condition of moisture. The belt of singing sand is best developed in the zone which is periodically bathed by the waves. Since the water of the lake contains calcium and magnesium bicarbonates, Richardson believes that these coat the surfaces and that it is the rubbing of such surfaces which produces the peculiar note.[1] Chemical analyses which he conducted failed, however, to reveal any trace of this film. He attributes the absence of the sound in the dune sand to the leaching action of the rain and the removal of the film by abrasion. The upper limit of the singing sand area is, however, not reached by waves for weeks; and during this time the wind may entirely change the arrangement of the sand. Salts deposited by evaporation do not appear, therefore, to offer a satisfactory explanation.

A certain degree of moisture seems to be more probable as the chief cause. At a depth of a few inches below the singing sand belt the sand is notably moist; and that portion above apparently receives a less amount of moisture from this lower reservoir. Along the gentle slope of the beach near the water this condition is best fulfilled, whereas in the dunes or along the upper beach the moist zone lies too deep. In the dunes, however, a somewhat similar sound may be produced if the foot is jammed below the very dry surface layer. The resinous tone is also sometimes distinguishable in the surface dune sands after a rain. That the phenomenon is related to

[1] W. D. Richardson, "Singing Sands of Lake Michigan," *Science*, new series, L (1919), 494.

moisture rather than salts is suggested also by two other lines of evidence. During work in Allegan County, Michigan, the Bureau of Soils shipped a sample of the sand to Washington in a sack. When examined there some months later, after it had dried, the musical quality had entirely disappeared. The sand of Rockaway Beach, New York, possesses this same quality; and Fairchild describes some which he has had in a closed bottle for 35 years and which, when opened, still gave the high singing note. Upon exposure in a warm dry room it soon lost its sonorous quality.[1] Fippin describes the necessary amount of moisture as "somewhere in the region of the lento-capillary point or the margin between hygroscopic and free capillary moisture."[2]

[1] *Science*, new series, LI (1920), 63.
[2] *Ibid.*, p. 64.

CHAPTER IV

EOLIAN ACTIVITY

MOVEMENT OF SAND BY THE WIND

THE NATURE OF SAND MOVEMENT

The wind moves sand either by rolling it along the ground or by sweeping it up and forward. In the latter case the advance commonly consists of short jumps, the grain being carried from a fraction of an inch to many feet, then dropped, only to be again swept on by a later gust. With grains of a fairly uniform size it seems very doubtful whether true rolling by the wind is a process of much importance. Since, in proportion to the size of the grain to be moved, the land surface is far from smooth, movement consists very largely in the sand being bounced along. Where coarse sand is scattered above compacted finer sand, rolling may take place; and where fine sand is sliding down a slope at the angles of rest the grains roll. However, a careful study of the movement of sand in the dunes emphasizes the importance of saltation, the grains being lifted and carried in short jumps.

Movement of the sand assumes two forms. Above the point known as the first critical velocity of the wind, at which movement is initiated, ripples are formed. There is then a second critical velocity beyond which all ripples are destroyed and the sand is blown in streamers or sheets. It is only with the lowest wind velocities that approximate rolling can take place, if at all. Blowing sand in this region is largely confined to within a few inches of the surface, except where there is an abrupt drop in the topography and the sand is blown out parallel with the former surface. Such is the case with the so-called "smoking dunes," where a high wind moving up the windward side "takes off" at the crest and fine sand streams out to leeward. Bits of glass lying on the surface are rounded and frosted by abrasion from the driven sand, while windows a few feet above the ground commonly remain clear. Only with high turbulent winds or special topographic relations does the blown sand rise more than a very few feet above the surface.

The size, shape, and composition of the grain are of much importance. Heavier or larger grains are less easily lifted and they progress by shorter jumps, while the finest products of abrasion can be picked up by much more gentle breezes and may not settle until outside the dune area. On

22

surfaces which have been compacted, as by rain or snow, the individual grains tend to interlock and the wind does not so easily move them.

In order to determine the actual velocities necessary for sand movement, measurements were made under different conditions in various parts of the area. A 6-inch windmill-type Keuffel and Esser anemometer with vertical blades was used. The data from many observations indicate that, with common beach and dune sand, transportation begins with a wind velocity of 6.8 miles per hour. The wind, however, is very gusty. And since measurements could not be made for periods of less than 6–12 seconds, while the individual gusts last only 2 or 3 seconds, it is obvious that the velocity of the wind during the gusts was not accurately obtained. It is thought, however, that 6.8 miles per hour is very close to the velocity required to start sand movement. Udden has stated that "the velocity in the layer [of wind] next to the surface of the ground probably never reaches 3 miles per hour";[1] but on surfaces inclined to face the wind it is certain that there are higher surface velocities. In the Libyan Desert, with a recording anemometer one meter above the surface, Beadnell found that "On the dunes the sand commences to move when the wind attains the velocity of a light breeze, or 13 miles per hour. The wind becomes visibly charged with sand at 23 miles per hour . . . . ," while in sand storms velocities are as high as 34 miles per hour.[2]

Velocities measured with anemometers at considerable heights above the ground are obviously not the same as those next the surface. For the purpose of securing some comparison of these surface winds with movements at higher elevations the anemometer was read on the ground and also at an elevation of 6 feet. On the basis of twelve comparisons the ratio of the surface velocities to those at 6 feet was .688, or approximately 2 to 3. The United States Weather Bureau has recently conducted similar experiments in California with Robinson cup anemometers.[3] One instrument was placed 1 foot above the surface and the second at 10 feet. As the result of 127 comparative measurements, the velocities have a ratio of .486, or approximately 1 to 2.[4] In order to obtain some comparison of surface

[1] John A. Udden, "The Mechanical Composition of Wind Deposits, Rock Island, Illinois," *Augustana Library Publication No. 1* (1898), p. 24.

[2] H. J. L. Beadnell, "Sand Dunes of the Libyan Desert," *Geographical Journal*, XXXV (1910), 386.

[3] Personal communication from Mr. B. C. Kadel.

[4] B. C. Kadel, "Anemometer Records on a Buffalo Office Building Compared with Those Secured near the Surface of the Lake," *Monthly Weather Review*, XLV (1917), 156–59.

movement with velocities at the University of Chicago station, where the elevation of the instruments above the ground is 131 feet, the windmill anemometer was exposed on the open surface of the Midway Plaisance, 200 yards distant. On the basis of four observations on different days and with different wind directions, the ratio of surface to station was found to be .275, approximately 1 to 4. Since the dunes are 20–35 miles from the University, and the conditions of exposure and velocity quite different, this relation can be no more than suggestive. It at least seems clear that the surface velocity in the dunes becomes sufficiently high for extensive sand movement only with strong winds, and that gales are of especial importance, probably a single one producing greater results than several months of gentle breezes.

THE SAND GRAINS

COMPLEX DEVELOPMENT

The sand grains now making up the dunes have had a long and complex history. They have been handled not only by the wind and waves, but doubtless by glaciers and rivers as well. It is at once seen that moving sand on the surface of dunes is constantly abraded, gradually wearing the grains smaller and smaller and making them rounder and rounder. But since all the sand of a dune, even though it is now buried or pinned down by vegetation, was at one time at the surface, it must have been similarly abraded and rounded in the past.

Since the beach is obviously the source of the sand now in the dunes, it has apparently been transported by wave action from pre-existing deposits exposed farther up the lake, probably at least fifty miles away. But during the vicissitudes of this journey under the influence of waves and littoral currents the individual grains doubtless traveled many times this distance. During the surge and swash of the waves the grains must have been hurled onto the beach and dragged back into the lake innumerable times in the course of a mile of travel along the shore. It is also entirely likely that reversed littoral currents swept the grains backwards at times. During this transportation doubtless the grains suffered also some eolian wear, for there must have been many grains left stranded on the wide beaches, blown about by the wind, and eventually blown back into the lake. Under the stress of transportation the softer fragments were ground to mud and silt fine enough to remain in suspension and be washed out to settle in deep quiet water far from shore. Thus practically only the quartz grains, due to their greater resistance to wear and their relative lightness, survived the long transportation.

The material transported by the waves had its source, in turn, in the glacial drift which composes the shores of the lake in their central and northern portions. The material of the drift was picked up, transported, and deposited by glacial ice. During transportation the grains were abraded, reducing many of the larger fragments to particles of sand, silt, and clay. Glacial sand grains show fresh fractures, faceted faces, and typically little rounding. But many of the grains even in the drift are well rounded showing that the glacier must have overridden a sandstone and thus acquired grains which were already rounded. How these grains became round is only a matter of inference and conjecture, for the story becomes more and more obscure when traced into antiquity.

EOLIAN VERSUS AQUEOUS TEXTURAL CRITERIA

Previous study of sand grains has been undertaken largely in order to establish criteria for the interpretation of sedimentary rocks. Investigators have endeavored to obtain criteria for determining whether a given sandstone was formed under water or whether it was a wind-laid deposit. Since the dunes are but a geologic formation in the making, they offer an opportunity for evaluating the various proposed criteria. It is widely recognized that no set of characteristics of the sand itself can alone finally settle the question of its origin or mode of deposition, for that problem requires a knowledge of field relationships. The evidence of eolian wear may be distinct, but is not a proof of deposition under eolian conditions; it merely indicates that such wear has taken place at some time during the history of the sand.

The more important of the textural criteria by which sands have been interpreted as of eolian instead of aqueous origin are as follows:

1. Size.
   a) Uniformity of grain, usually between .125 and .500 mm.
   b) Second largest percentage of size is coarser than the size of the largest percentage.
2. Roundness.
   Many below .1 mm.; lowest, .03 mm.
3. Mat or "frosted" surface.
4. Absence of heavy minerals.
5. Character of minerals.
   Small ratio of cleavable to non-cleavable.
   Small ratio of soft to hard.

1. *Size.*—(a) Wind-blown sand may be far more uniform in size than that handled by water, whereas in aqueous deposits the particles range from clay to bowlders. Dune sand is confined to the narrow range of .03

mm. to 2.0 mm. Material finer than this is easily carried in suspension by the air and is lost to the dune area, while coarse sand and pebbles cannot readily be moved by the wind and so are very rare in dune deposits. By far the largest percentage of dune sand is between .125 and .500 mm. While it is thus true that eolian sands are uniform, it does not follow that aqueous sands are necessarily not uniform. The ultimate source of sand is largely the crystals of igneous rocks which average but slightly larger than eolian grains. With the absence of large units in the source of supply and the removal of the finer clays by suspension in moving water, aqueous sands may be fully as uniform as dune sand and the criteria of uniformity has no conclusive value.

(b) Since the wind is much more effective in moving fine particles than coarse, the smaller products of abrasion are carried away from the dune area and the resultant sand is therefore relatively free from the smaller grains. Originally proposed by Udden, this principle may be interpreted as follows: If the sand be divided into classes of size, the second-largest percentage will be found on the coarser side of the largest percentage. Or, as stated by Dake, "if the total coarser than the maximum grade is greater than the total finer than the maximum grade, the sand is more probably eolian." Since water may be equally as effective as wind in removing small grains, this second phase of sand size is of very doubtful value. Experimental work by Dake bears this out.

2. *Roundness.*—One of the most frequent criteria of eolian origin has been the roundness of the sand. It has been thought that sand grains tend to become more rounded under the action of the air than under that of water, and this process takes place more rapidly and extends to smaller-sized grains. When sand is wet, each grain is surrounded by a film of water, held by adsorption and surface tension, which acts as a buffer and protects the grains against sharp impacts. The sand is furthermore buoyed up by the water and grains do not strike with the fullest possible momentum. In the air velocities are higher and the grains come together in direct contact. Since the surface film of water becomes more protective with decreasing size of the grain and its consequent loss of weight, some writers have theoretically established a minimum point below which grains cannot be rounded by water. Given sufficient time and the impact of storm waves, however, it seems probable that if such a limit exists it is only reached when the grain becomes very small (Galloway). Well-rounded wind-worn grains have been measured down to 0.034 mm. by Fruh,[1] and grains below .1 are usually abundant.

[1] Quoted by Goldman, *American Journal of Science,* new series, XXXIX (1915), 272.

As a generalization, it is true that wind-blown sand is more rounded than water-worn sand, and that the lower limit of rounding is smaller with air than with water. However, since the time element is so large a factor, it is usually impossible to say whether a sand of a certain degree of roundness is the product of rapid eolian wear or of aqueous wear during a longer period of time. The time factor appears to control very largely and, in the absence of knowledge as to its duration, the roundness of the sand can be only suggestive. In fact, recent experimental work seems to show that aqueous wear is more rapid than eolian (Anderson).

3. *Surface.*—While the degree of rounding thus has but doubtful diagnostic value, one other factor seems to be of real distinction. This is the character of the surface. Grains rounded by water have smooth pearly surfaces, while grains rounded by air are dull and pitted. When seen under a microscope the latter appear frosted rather than bright, and, in addition to the frosting, there may be small pits. Although the surface appears frosted upon magnification, in reality the dulness is more of a mat surface, and is best so described, being of a much finer texture than common frosted glass. This condition is a result of the nature of the impact under the air and appears to be practically the only criterion of positive value. Higgins has pointed out that with wet grindstones a smooth surface is produced, while the surface is pitted and frosted when the grinding is dry.[1]

It has not been demonstrated that such a mat surface can be produced under water; and where such a feature is present it clearly indicates eolian conditions at some late time during the development of the sand.

4. *Absence of heavy minerals.*—In wind-blown deposits which have been moved a considerable distance by the wind, minerals with a high specific gravity are largely absent, having been left behind because of their weight and the consequent inability of the air at normal velocities to move them. Galloway states that minerals with a specific gravity between 4 and 5 will constitute less than 5 per cent of the entire sand, while minerals with a specific gravity over 5 will usually be absent. With transportation by water, however, the individual grains are buoyed up, and beach sands containing heavy minerals are not uncommon. If, however, such minerals are not present in the source of supply, they will of course be absent in both beach and dune sands. This criterion must therefore be accompanied by field knowledge of the source of the material and may only be used with caution.

5. *Character of minerals.*—It is commonly held that with the vigorous

[1] *Bull. Geol. Soc. Amer.*, XXXIII (1922), 105.

abrasion under eolian conditions, due to higher velocities and direct con-
tacts, grains are worn more rapidly than by water. Thus those minerals
which are softer are rapidly pulverized and removed. Likewise cleavable
minerals are broken into fragments and are relatively rare in dune sands.
For example, mica is supposed never to be found in wind-blown sands.
Thus dune sands often have a smaller ratio of cleavable to non-cleavable,
and softer to harder, minerals than those produced under water. As with
the previous criteria, however, the time element and the source of supply
entirely invalidate this line of evidence in the absence of additional data.

VALUE OF TEXTURAL CRITERIA IN THIS AREA

In the light of the foregoing general criteria, attention will now be directed to samples of sand from this particular area. The original purpose
of this survey was the consideration of changes in the sand through wear
by water and wind, and the present scope has been enlarged as the result
of field and laboratory work. It was originally anticipated that distinct
differences would be found under different conditions, such as the upper
and lower beaches, the windward side of dunes, the crest and the lee side
of blowouts, and the fact that the sand would show a progressive diminu-
tion in size of grain from the shore dunes landward. The present interpretation of the dunes renders any such distinctions improbable and of very
little diagnostic value. In an earlier publication the writer presented forty-
one mechanical analyses based upon samples from all parts of the
dunes.[1] These analyses showed considerable latitude, but are largely to be
explained as due to chance local variations or conditions of subsequent
exposure. Since the earlier observations are now given but little weight
and were made with sieves of a different calibration from those shortly to
be described, they are not here repeated.

As has been outlined, the material of the dunes is derived from the till
of the eastern and western shores of the lake and has had a complex history. In addition to the samples previously referred to, many others have
been collected and the following study is based upon nearly ninety samples. The various criteria will now be considered in their relation to this
area.

Size.—In the determination of the size of grain, the samples were
grouped under seven heads. A composite sample of each of these was ana-
lyzed and the results are tabulated below. The sieves employed were made
by the W. S. Tyler Company, of Cleveland, Ohio, and were calibrated in
accordance with the Bureau of Standards specifications and the sugges-

[1] G. B. Cressey, *Studies in the Sand Dunes of Northwestern Indiana* (1921), p. 45.

tions of Wentworth.[1] The ratio between the different sizes of the screen scale is 1.414 or $\sqrt{2}$, so that the width of the opening in each successive sieve bears this ratio to the previous sieve. Thus the area of the opening of any one size is just double or half that of the adjacent size, and the areas have the constant ratio of 2. The sieves were placed one above the other and the tower was shaken for ten minutes by a mechanical shaker. The percentage weights are shown in Table II.

TABLE II

TABLE OF RELATIVE SIZES

Openings			Till	Illinois Beach	Indiana Beach	Main Dune Complex	Blowouts	Former Beaches	Interior Dune Belts
Millimeters	Inches	Mesh to the Inch	A	B	C	D	E	F	G
>.500	.0197	35	16.95	.33	.20	.74	5.20	1.00	.54
>.353	.0138	45	4.38	2.33	4.90	5.00	7.70	4.50	3.60
>.250	.0098	60	8.48	27.16	40.14	29.10	42.02	15.64	18.90
>.177	.0070	80	7.60	45.83	40.50	44.80	34.90	34.82	33.86
>.125	.0049	120	12.85	22.50	13.04	20.10	10.04	39.90	38.94
<.125	.0049	120	49.85	1.50	.90	.38	.24	4.20	4.34
Total			100.11	99.65	99.68	100.12	100.10	100.06	100.18

A. Two samples of till, Fort Sheridan and Wilmette.
B. Three samples from the western beach in Illinois (Lake Forest, Fort Sheridan, Wilmette).
C. Eleven samples from the present beach in Indiana, Stockton to Sheridan Beach.
D. Thirty-nine samples from the main dune complex, including nine samples of "E."
E. Nine samples from blowouts now active, Miller to Michigan City.
F. Nine samples from former beach lines.
G. Eleven samples from interior dune belts related to higher shore lines.

In the migration of the sand from the till bluffs to the dunes certain features may be pointed out. It is at once apparent that the sand both of the dunes and of the beach is almost entirely between $\frac{1}{2}$ and $\frac{1}{8}$ millimeter in diameter, so that the criterion of size is, here at least, valueless. Likewise the criterion of the second-highest percentage of size is not borne out. In the earlier analyses previously referred to, nineteen out of thirty-three dune samples and five out of eight beach samples showed the second-highest percentage on the coarser side of the highest.

Rounding and mat surface.—In view of the fact that considerable im-

[1] Chester K. Wentworth, "A Scale of Grade and Size for Clastic Sediments," *Journal of Geology*, XXX (1922), 377–92.

portance has been attached to rounding as a criterion of eolian origin, especial attention was given to it by the writer. It was very much hoped that a definite quantitative scale could be developed to cover the degree of roundness, but although numerous experiments were tried, no satisfactory basis for such work was devised. In order to afford some basis for tabulation, six rather arbitrary classes or grades were chosen, ranging from completely angular to spherical and covering eolian versus aqueous wear. These are not strictly equal in value, for, in the history of one grain, the passage from angularity to partial rounding is much more rapid than from partial rounding to sphericity. Since the relative time values are unknown, the following scale for the degree of rounding is imperfect to that degree. It refers only to quartz sand, and is as follows:

Class 1: The grains are sharply angular, with glistening conchoidal fractures. No corners are rounded and the surface is fresh, without mat or polish (Plate VII, *a*).

Class 2: The grains show a few conchoidal fractures and some of the corners are rounded. The surface is less shiny but does not show a pearly polish (Plate VII, *b*).

Class 3: There are no fracture surfaces, but the grains are still more angular than round. The corners are smoothed off and the surface is pearly or dull, though without the mat appearance (Plate VII, *c*).

Class 4: The grains are slightly more round than with Class 3, and both the mat surface and pitting first appear. Wind work has smoothed rather than shaped the grain (Plate VII, *d*).

Class 5: The grain is subspherical or bean-shaped. There are no corners and the grain is fully covered with the mat surface and possibly with the pitting. The ratio of maximum to minimum diameters is not more than $2\frac{1}{2}$ to 1. Wind work has shaped the grain (Plate VII, *e*).

Class 6: The grain is fairly spherical with the surface, as in Class 5. The ratio of the diameters is not over $1\frac{1}{2}$ to 1 (Plate VII, *f*).

In place of the composite analyses made for the size of the grains, each one of seventy-five samples of sand was examined separately with a binocular microscope and the percentage of each class determined visually. This of course involves a personal error; but, despite numerous repetitions, in no case did the estimate of any particular class vary more than 5 per cent. Table III shows the average results for each of the localities described under the size of the sand.

An inspection of this table at once brings out certain facts which are more definite and probably of more value than the analyses with regard to size. Well-rounded grains are present in all of the beach and dune samples, but in a comparison of B, C, D, and E it is clear that eolian sands are more rounded. Blowouts represent the climax of wind activity and the contrast with the Illinois Beach is pronounced. The relative coarseness of F and G from the former beaches and interior dune belts is no doubt due to the relative shortness of the time during which they were being formed.

Even more than indicated by the table, the mat surface is characteristic of the dune sand and appears to be the distinguishing criterion of eolian action. The presence of such grains in beach sands is no doubt related to wind work on the beach.

Due to the greater mass of larger grains or those of higher specific gravity, it is noticeable that the larger or heavier the grain, the better it is rounded. Thus practically no large angular grains are found; and, though

TABLE III

Class	Till*	Illinois Beach	Indiana Beach	Main Dune Complex	Blowouts	Former Beaches	Interior Dune Belts
	A	B	C	D	E	F	G
1	15	12	7	6	5	10	9
2	30	13	13	13	12	17	15
3	35	33	26	30	23	32	35
4	15	23	31	32	33	26	27
5	5	12	15	13	19	10	10
6	0	7	8	6	8	5	4

*This applies only to grains larger than .177 mm. Smaller particles almost exclusively belong to classes 1 and 2.

the great bulk of a sample may be angular, there may be a few well-rounded grains of larger size (Class 5).

Absence of heavy minerals.—The most abundant of the heavy minerals in the sand is magnetite, which has a specific gravity of 5.17 (quartz, 2.66). Along the beach it often forms a veneer upon the quartz sand, having been separated by natural placer methods. These deposits may cover several square yards, and in part the magnetite is derived from the slag of the steel mills, it being abundant in the darker varieties. Magnetite is also found in the present fore dune ridge and in blowouts, and, while it is not abundant, it is often easily noticeable. A few grains are found in the samples from the established dunes, so that its presence cannot be taken as a criterion of non-eolian sand.

Character of minerals.—The sand of both beach and dunes is very largely quartz. In the process of the microscopic examination of the rounding, note was made of grains other than quartz, and in no case did rapid inspection show more than 15 per cent. In most of the beach and dune sands, quartz grains constitute more than 90 per cent of the sample. Other minerals are principally the feldspars, but magnetite, garnet, zircon, and a variety of less important minerals are also present. Especially in the beach sands and also in the crests of the coarser ripples there are numerous fragments of fine-textured igneous rocks (Plate VIII, *b*). These have been worn down to sand size, but are usually at least half a millimeter in diameter.

Very soft and cleavable minerals are soon reduced to silt particles during transportation from the till, and are left deposited in the lake. Less friable or soft minerals reach the dune area rounded and fractured but still large enough to be identified. Magnetite is the most abundant of the heavy minerals and, because of its high specific gravity, it strikes other grains with a stronger impact and is rapidly rounded. No angular magnetite has been seen, its degree of rounding commonly ranging from Class 3 to Class 5 (Plate VII, *c* and *e*).

While other criteria of origin may be applicable to sands of other regions, the mat surface of the sand grains alone seems to be a diagnostic eolian criterion for the dune sands of this Lake Michigan region.

RIPPLE MARKS

Eolian ripple marks, both on exposed surfaces of the dunes and on the beach, are abundant in the dune country. Broadly defined, they include all minor irregularities of the surface due to ruffling by the wind. Commonly they consist of small wavelike ridges whose windward slopes are more gentle than the leeward ones. Less common forms are those developed by local oscillations of the wind in the lee of sticks, stones, etc.

FORMS

There are two common forms of ripples in the Indiana dunes. In the first form all the sand is of approximately the same size, while in the second form the ripple itself is composed of much coarser grains and is built on a surface of normal dune sand. In the first, the ripple and the substratum are similar, both being largely of quartz sand; in the second, the ripple differs from the substratum, the fragments in the ripple being largely heavier and usually darker. The pattern of this second kind is also less uniform. These two types are illustrated on Plate VIII. The first or uniform-grained type is far more abundant and is quite regular; single ridges having been traced as much as 40 feet without break or union. The crests are spaced from 2 to 4 inches apart, and the height ranges from one-eighth to one-fourth of an inch from trough to crest. In the second or coarse-grained type there is considerable variation in size and pattern. As shown in Plate VIII, *b*, there are often both larger and smaller ripples together, and it is seldom that any one crest is continuous for more than 2 or 3 feet. The wave-length from crest to crest ranges from 4 inches to 2 feet, or exceptionally, with irregular forms, to about 6 feet.

ORIGIN

The origin of ripple marks has long been in dispute. Experiments and field studies by many observers in many places have failed to yield uniform theories. Cornish, one of the chief writers, years ago produced ripples in the laboratory "by the action of a steady artificial blast upon ordinary heterogeneous sand; but artificially assorted sand containing no fine particles was not thrown into ripples."[1] He emphasizes the importance of fine sand which can be lifted by the wind eddy in the lee of larger grains, and believes that rippling of sand takes place only when the eddy in the lee of the larger grains is of sufficient strength to lift the smaller ones. In contrast, however, King largely minimizes the influence of a lee eddy in originating the ripple. "When the wind blows over an unrippled surface of sand or over a rippled surface from a new direction, it first moves those grains which from their size, shape, position, or other cause are in the condition of most unstable equilibrium."[2] The first development seems to be the formation of shallow pits due in part to the exposure to the wind and also no doubt to whorls in the air. The development of ripples from these first pits is attributed by King to their lateral expansion, and their regular spacing to waves in the air due to the surface contact. Baschin attributes regular ripples to the tendency to form a Helmholtz wave surface under the friction of the passing wind.[3] Bucher[4] has recently given much attention to ripples, especially the subaqueous forms, and he largely follows King as to their origin. He emphasizes the fact that "the vortices are not the essential element in the formation of current ripples" and points out that "a sinuous surface of contact between a fluid (as the air) and a sediment offers a minimum of friction." He broadly defines ripples "to include all undulating surface forms which originate as surfaces of least friction along the contact between a moving fluid and an unconsolidating sediment."

[1] Vaughn Cornish, "On Kumatology," *Geographical Journal*, XIII (1899), 624.

[2] W. J. Harding King, "The Nature and Formation of Ripples and Dunes," *Geographical Journal*, XLVII (1916), 204.

[3] Quoted by King, *op. cit.*, p. 203.

[4] Walter H. Bucher, "The Origin of Ripples and Related Sedimentary Surface Forms," *American Journal of Science*, 3d series, XLVII (1919), 149–210.

On the basis of many measurements, Cornish has established the ratio of the wave-length to height in wind ripples as 18 to 1, regardless of the size of the ripple. Since this is approximately the same as that of waves at sea and also agrees with the measurements for some belts of dunes, he classes them all as wave phenomena. As will be pointed out under the consideration of dune movement, the nature of sand transportation is so different from the movement of a fluid that the likeness of ripples and dunes to waves is only superficial.

As has been pointed out previously, the formation of ripple marks takes place between two critical velocities. The lower of these is that at which sand movement begins, a figure which varies with the size, shape, composition, and position of the grains, but is about 6.8 miles per hour. Various theories of ripple origin have been outlined; but once the form has been developed, the individual grains roll or bounce along up the windward side of the ripple and fall over the crest, where they either lie at the angle of rest or are further moved by the lee eddy. The rate of advance of the ripple varies inversely with its size and directly with the strength of the wind, but is modified by the size of grain and character of the ripple. An advance of a foot an hour would be quite rapid. At a second and higher velocity, which likewise is dependent upon various factors, the mode of transportation of the sand changes and the ripples disappear. At this velocity of the wind, the sand is whirled from crest to crest in one leap so that the ripples grow less distinct in form and finally disappear, leaving a comparatively even surface over which the sand is blown in sheets or streamers. This second critical velocity is about 20 miles per hour.

PRESERVATION OF RIPPLES

Despite the fact that ripple marks are exceedingly abundant on the surface of the dunes, practically no buried ripples are exposed in cross-sections. Eolian cross-bedding and stratification planes are found in most vertical exposures, but only two or three cases of preserved ripples have been found by the writer.

SUBAERIAL VERSUS SUBAQUEOUS

Subaerial ripple marks differ from the subaqueous current and oscillation ripples in having the coarser particles on the crest, whereas those forms developed under water have the larger grains in the trough, the explanation being that in wind-developed types the finer grains are blown away from the crests, whereas with water ripples the current is not strong enough to lift the coarser and heavier grains out of the troughs.

DUNE ACCUMULATION

CAUSES

The accumulation of sand into dunes is due either to (1) the checking of the sand-laden wind by some obstacle, such as vegetation, thus diminishing its carrying capacity and resulting in deposition of sand, or (2) the overtaking of larger ripples by smaller ones. The most frequently stated reason for dune formation is the obstruction formed by vegetation. Whenever a sand-laden wind is checked by grasses or trees it drops some of its load and, in the case of isolated obstructions or clumps of vegetation, a "lee dune" is formed in and behind the obstacle (Plate IX, *b*). Such accumulations are very common in this area and range in size from a few inches high and a foot or so long to heights of 10 feet and lengths of 25 feet or more. When the wind shifts, the tails of these lee dunes are likewise turned so that they are under the protecting lee of the obstacles. In areas which are especially exposed to shifting winds, as, for example, on bare surfaces of the higher dunes, these sand accumulations about clumps of vegetation lose their tails of sand and become conical; they are then known as "turret dunes" (Plate IX, *a*). Where the obstructing vegetation is linear rather than in isolated clumps, as, for example, at the inner margin of the beach, the dune accumulation takes the form of a ridge.

Accumulations such as those just described are due to a decrease in the wind velocity caused by the obstacles. Similar results are produced by obstructions other than vegetation, which also check the wind, such as the open fence illustrated in Plate X, *a*. If the fence were tight so that no wind could pass through it, eddies would be formed on both sides and these would scour the sand and undermine the fence; any accumulation which might take place would be a few feet either side of the fence. One of the most effective means of building a protective dune to check migration or cause accumulation is therefore to place a line of 4-foot uprights in the sand with an open space of a few inches between them. As the sand builds up about them they may then be raised. Upon the same principle of diminished velocity, dunes may be formed in the lee of other dunes, or even of buildings, or where cross-wind currents cause a lull.

The second process of dune accumulation is based upon the unequal movement of ripple marks. These forms obey the same law of movement which applies to dunes, namely, that the rate of advance is directly proportional to the velocity of the wind and inversely proportional to the mass of the ripple. Thus small ripples advance more rapidly than larger forms and will overtake them. When two ripples have thus coalesced, the mass of the new ripple is greater and its rate of advance is checked. However, ripples to the windward are unaffected and continue at their former speed, finally advancing up the slope of the large ripple and combining with it (Fig. 1). By this cumulative process the sand aggregation passes out of the ripple class and becomes a dune. Just where the change in name should be applied is doubtful, but it would seem best to use the term ripple for those undulating forms produced as surfaces of least friction between air and sand, and to apply the term dune when cumulative piling up begins. Thus ripples are forms related to surfaces of equilibrium, whereas dunes represent sand aggregation due to diminished carrying

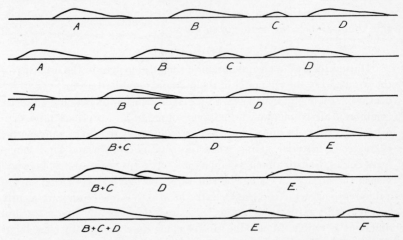

FIG. 1.—The formation of dunes through the overtake of ripples. In the migration of the ripples, from right to left, *C* overtakes and merges with *B*, which then moves more slowly and is then overtaken by *D*.

capacity of additive processes. This second mode of dune formation has commonly been overlooked in the literature, but it seems to be of large importance, especially in the great sandy deserts where there is no vegetation or other obstacles to cause accumulation. Likewise the dunes formed in this area at the highest stage of the lake, when the glacial ice had just withdrawn from the Valparaiso Moraine, were presumably free from vegetation, and ripple overtake may have been the dominant factor in their initiation.

WIND DIRECTIONS

The direction of the wind plays a large part in dune accumulation. Where winds are predominantly from one direction, much more regular forms arise and the dunes are linear; the movement of the dune is likewise pronounced. With variable winds accumulation takes place, but the result is a more or less circular hill in place of a ridge. Where a large area is involved, uniform winds produce a series of parallel ridges, while variable winds build a dune complex. The strength of the wind determines whether linear dunes shall be parallel or at right angles to the wind direction, the latter being common under low velocities, the former under higher velocities.

In the Indiana area winds from the lake are most effective, since they approach the dunes from the beach and thus find exposures of sand available for movement and accumulation. Coming off the smooth surface of the lake these winds also have higher average velocities. Winds from other directions strike the dune complex where it is forested. Dune accumulation thus parallels the source of supply.

STRATIFICATION

During the eolian accumulation of sand differences in the intensity of the wind and in the character of the material deposited give rise to stratification, visible upon erosion. Such stratification or bedding surfaces, common in all sedimentary formations, represent interruptions in the depositional record. In dune sand they are commonly due to a change in the character of material. Thus, when the wind dies down and sand movement ceases, a small amount of dust may settle out of the atmosphere and veneer the surface. A change in wind direction may likewise bring sand of a different character and produce stratification. While erosion frequently reveals such stratification surfaces, it is only occasionally that a textural difference is visible. Where the sand of older dunes is partially consolidated through cementation by clay particles, iron oxide, or calcium carbonate, the stratification is especially evident. Plate X, *a*, shows such an exposure where the cementation along the several planes causes them to stand out in relief. In this case the cement is iron oxide derived from the finer particles which settled during calms.

Eolian cross-bedding commonly shows sweeping curves which slope in various directions and with various angles, none, however, steeper than 32°. Horizontal beds are absent and many beds are tangent one to another; hence the term tangential bedding. Such bedding, however, is relatively rare in the Indiana dunes, the common attitudes recording either gentle windward or steep lee slopes.

FORMS OF DUNES

In general, dunes may be grouped in two large divisions: (1) those formed along shores, either ocean or lake, and (2) those in interior areas

such as deserts, the flood plains of sandy intermittent rivers, and playas.
Dunes are by no means confined to arid climates, though it is true that
conditions there are commonly more favorable. The second type is here
but incidentally mentioned, while discussion of the first type is largely
confined to the forms developed at the southern end of Lake Michigan.
Here the dunes, both of the present and the former shore lines, are definitely related to the beach as the source of supply. Other similar dune
areas are found in Gascony and in New Zealand.

The dune complex at the southern end of Lake Michigan is largely
composed of two characteristic dune types, the *fore dune* (Plates XI, *b;*
XII; XIII, *a;* XV, *a;* XVI, *b*) and the *blowout dune* (Plates III, *a;* XIII, *b;*
XIV; XV; XVI, *a*). In addition there are minor forms related directly to
vegetation, such as the lee (Plate IX, *b*) and turret dunes (Plate IX, *a*).
These two principal forms (fore dune and blowout dune) in various com-
binations comprise the great bulk of the entire complex. The fore dune
is essentially a ridge parallel to the shore and built just beyond the reach
of the highest waves. Its linear character is due in part to the influence of
the lake winds, in part to the belt of vegetation which springs up beyond
the beach margin, and largely to the supply of sand. Blowout dunes are
commonly developed along the shore by the action of the wind in scouring
out through the established dunes a passage which later is widened, deep-
ened, and extended inland. At their maximum development their windward slopes resemble large amphitheaters. Each form will now be considered in detail.

THE FORE DUNE

ORIGIN AND RELATIONSHIP

On most sandy shores where the formation of dunes is in progress, the
fore dune is the characteristic type at the edge of the beach (Plate XI, *b*).
Typically it is a more or less regular ridge partially covered with trees and
grasses. The lee slope approaches the angle of rest, i.e., 32°, while the
windward slope is more gentle, usually about 10°. The development of a
fore dune takes place only on wide and rather flat beaches, where there is
an abundant supply of sand and effective on-shore winds. Vegetation,
such as the various grasses, the sand cherry, etc., springs up beyond the
reach of the storm waves and finds moisture at a slight depth. By the process already described accumulation results in a linear arrangement. Ide-
ally this process should produce a continuous ridge, and, while such is often
the case, the early stages are more often marked by low elongated hills.
As accumulation continues and the sand becomes more stable, cottonwoods spring up and are of importance in the later stages of accumulation.

So long as the supply of sand continues and the beach remains the same width, the fore dune ridge continues to grow in height and width. When a certain elevation is reached, however, the higher and stronger upper winds carry sand away as rapidly as it can be brought up the windward slope. Thus a maximum and roughly uniform height is established by an equilibrium between the ability of the surface winds to move sand up the dune and the erosive force of the higher winds. Due to the many factors of exposure, vegetation, abundance of supply, etc., this figure varies, usually being between 50 and 75 feet, though in some cases reaching 100 feet in height.

Fore dunes normally form only on beaches which are receiving a continual supply of sand, part of which goes to the construction of the dune and part to the widening of the beach. The formation of fore dunes is determined by conditions at the inner margin of the active beach. When the beach is sufficiently widened by accretion on the lakeward margin, a new ridge arises in front of the older fore dune (Plate XIII, *a*). By the continuation of this process, a series of parallel ridges may arise, each at one time having been the fore dune and each roughly marking a position of the shore line. As each fore dune comes under the protection of a new ridge between it and the on-shore winds, it is sheltered and the sand becomes anchored under a protective veneer of vegetation. Each fore dune is completed with but little landward movement, and it serves as a protection to the hinterland by gathering up the sand blown in from the beach.

In the dune complex of Indiana, fore dunes are now being built in two general situations, namely: (1) broad beaches where sand is accumulating, and (2) across the entrance to large blowouts. Fore dune development at present centers around Miller Beach, extending to Gary on the west and a few miles beyond the former mouth of the Grand Calumet River on the east. Here at the head of the lake the littoral drift supplies sand to widen the beach and a new fore dune is being constructed. Around the Gary municipal bath house, east of Miller Beach, there is a well developed fore dune 40–50 feet high, and on the lakeward side a series of elongate hills averaging 20 feet high, which mark the beginning of the new ridge. Farther to the east the character of the shore changes from constructional to erosional and the fore dune proper disappears. Where the beach is wider locally accumulation may take place somewhat as indicated, but in place of a definite ridge, the sand merely piles up against the eroded shore face of the older dunes.

Fore dunes are also being built across the entrances to many of the larger blowouts. Although these may be located where shore erosion is dominant, their rather level floors, extending directly inland from the beach, in effect make the beach wider. Since sand is available from that in transit by littoral drift along the beach, the requisites for a fore dune are met.

PREVIOUS DEVELOPMENT

Although fore dunes are now forming in but a limited portion of the dune country, ridges parallel to the shore are abundant in the forested dune complex (Plate XII). These ridges represent former positions of the shore line and each in turn was at the time of its formation the fore dune. In part these ridges are still straight and regular; but with the many opportunities for wind erosion since their formation, not only are minor irregularities common, but large variations from the original form have developed in some localities. These ridges are well defined southeast of the former mouth of the Grand Calumet, around Dune Park, exceptionally well near the beach from Baileytown to Port Chester, northwest to north of Tamarack station, and to a limited extent east of Michigan City. In all parts of the dunes, both in the main complex and in the belts associated with the older and higher shore lines, there are former fore dune ridges. In fact the dune development in the interior belts was largely confined to the construction of a single fore dune at each successive stage.

BLOWOUT DUNES

CHARACTER

Blowout dunes or blowouts are among the characteristic features of the Lake Michigan dunes. Starting as small channels excavated by the wind in older dunes, they enlarge until they are great amphitheaters to the windward and have steep lee slopes (Plate XIV). In size the width ranges from a few feet up to several hundred yards; in length, to a quarter of a mile; and in height, to a maximum of 200 feet.

These great tongues of bare sand which project into the forest-covered complex are the most striking features of the landscape. While the term blowout is often applied merely to the hollow formed by the excavation, it would seem best to include the entire dune, since both windward and lee slopes are contemporaneous and monogenetic. By the earlier settlers they were known as "slides."

During the formation of a blowout its surface is largely free from vegetation and the wind vigorously erodes the windward slopes, carrying the sand up to the crest, where it falls down the lee slope. A cross-section of a fully developed blowout dune is almost flat near the beach, gradually steepening on the windward side to a maximum of 5°–8° near the crest. At the crest itself the profile is almost flat for a short distance and then abruptly descends in the lee slope (Fig. 2). As a result of many measurements on these lee slopes, the angle of rest of loose dry dune sand is found to be 32°, rarely varying even one degree. When wet or partially cemented, the sand may stand at a higher angle—even to verticality. The sides of blowouts may be steeper than any part of the longitudinal profile. In enlarging the blowout the wind undermines the sides and the sand slumps down. Due to incipient consolidation in the sand of the older dunes and the protecting mat of vegetation, this slope often exceeds 32°.

DISTRIBUTION

In distribution active blowout dunes are almost entirely confined to the present shore. Along the southern margin of the main dune complex the wind from across the meadow-like flat has an open sweep and there are a few areas of shifting sand and miniature blowouts. In the interior dune belts there are small blowouts at Miller, Tremont, and elsewhere. No normal active blowouts and very few patches of shifting sand occur within the dune complex, except as related to the present beach.

Similar blowouts are developed to a lesser extent in the coastal dunes of Gascony and New Zealand, and are also found in Nebraska and Illinois.

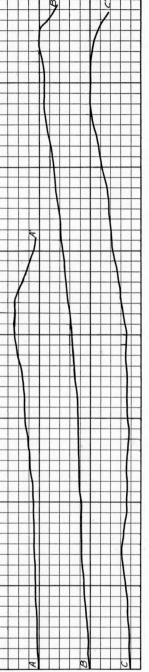

FIG. 2.—Cross-section of blowout dunes. Each square equals 25 feet, vertical and horizontal scales being the same. The sections start from lake level at the left and run N.–S. A–A', one-half mile east of Miller. B–B', Dune Park. C–C', north of Furnessville.

CAUSES OF ORIGIN

Blowouts are most extensively developed in old established dunes rather than in recent fore dune accumulations, for here the surface is stabilized and when cutting begins it is confined to a narrow and relatively deep channel in place of the broad scour characteristic in unprotected sand. Wherever the protecting veneer of vegetation is destroyed the bare sand is exposed directly to the wind and is shifted about. Where the exposure faces the stronger winds a blowout develops. Of the various ways in which the vegetation is broken, those for which man is responsible are numerous and important. Forest fires, the cutting of trees, the breaking of a trail, even a picnic camp, have all started the process. Other causes, such as fires from lightning, the uprooting of a tree, and the erosion of the shore face by waves, are all important. But the development of blowouts seems to have been greatly accelerated since the arrival of the white man. This is also true of other areas, for among the dunes associated with glacial lakes in Illinois, Gleason finds that there were no blowouts prior to the settlement of the land, but that they have been developed through the plowing of the fields and the removal of the timber.[1]

DEVELOPMENT

The development of blowout dunes follows a regular process and, except for interruptions, all blowouts have essentially the same history. Many more start than finish, for there is a continual contest between the erosive work of the wind and the hardy grasses which quickly spring up to blanket the sand. The ability of these grasses, of the cottonwoods, and of other forms of vegetation to thrive under apparently the most adverse conditions is a source of wonder. Even though buried to their tips they continue to grow, and on every surface during the summer where the wind ceases to erode or deposit for a few months they spring up. Thus only the most favorably situated wind channels develop into large blowouts, and a cessation of strong winds during a mild year may write the last chapter of the dune's activity.

Following the initiation of the wind channel all dimensions of the blowout are enlarged, the width always being at least three times the depth. If the blowout dune starts at the top of the present shore face, possibly in a former fore dune ridge, its slope toward the lake is at first rather steep, $10°–20°$, but as the cutting progresses inland the floor becomes flatter. The crest of the dune in the earlier stages is rather narrow, there being an abrupt transition from the gentle curve of the amphitheater to the $32°$ lee slope. By the addition of sand brought up the windward surface, the

[1] Gleason, *Bulletin Illinois State Laboratory of Natural History*, VII (1909), 144.

crest becomes higher and higher until it often rises above the surrounding ridges. It is thus exposed to winds from all directions and these check its upward growth, causing the crest to flatten out. In the advance of the blowout over established dunes there are often obstacles which deflect the course of the sand, causing the blowout to spread. Thus its breadth at the crest is often greater than at the mouth. Finally a certain size is reached beyond which the wind loses much of its effectiveness. The floor of the blowout becomes nearly flat and is essentially a landward extension of the beach. At this stage deposition commences across the mouth of the blowout and a fore dune ridge results (Plate XV, *a*). Since this new ridge of sand is not as high as the sides of the blowout, the wind is especially active through the opening and the accumulation of sand migrates up into the basin of the original blowout (Plate XV, *b*). The amphitheater thus becomes filled; and as the original crest is sheltered by the new blowout ridge to the windward, it is soon anchored by vegetation. The process may continue until the entire opening is filled and the original slope of the shore face is approximately restored. Mount Jensen, north of Johnsfield, is an interesting case of a triple blowout, one within another, all of which are now fixed by vegetation.

In some respects blowouts may be regarded as destructional phenomena. They occur in areas of established dunes and they entirely destroy the old topography, often burying forests which later may be uncovered. In places their advance is of economic detriment, for they may invade farms or cover railroads and highways. In another sense, however, blowout dunes represent definite construction, and are a normal rather than an abnormal type. While they do destroy the parallelism of ridges with the present shore, they are responsible for all of the highest elevations in the dune country. Whereas fore dune ridges rarely exceed 100 feet, the crests of blowouts rise to twice that height. Such blowouts as are involved in the highest elevations do not always have the amphitheater extensively developed, and the windward slope is usually above 10°. Due to shifting winds, the highest portions of such blowouts tend to be conical. Mount Tom (Plates VI, *a;* IX, *a*), at Waverly Beach, is the highest point in the area, and only the tops of trees on its summit now project above the sand. During the winter of 1922–23 at least two feet of sand were added to its height. It is now fully 200 feet above the lake.

VEGETATION AS A GEOLOGIC AGENT

Due to the abundant rainfall of the dune country, vegetation is luxuriant. Botanically there are many interesting relationships; but they are outside the scope of this study and for further details the reader is referred to the publications of Cowles and Downing, as listed in chapter vii. Vegetation is here considered only as a geologic agent, and in this respect its importance is largely in connection with erosion and deposition of sand by the wind. As a protective barrier it may be either in the form of a continuous blanket, as is the case in the older dunes, or it may merely consist of isolated grasses and shrubs with bare sand between. In the latter case the vegetation merely checks the wind, tending to reduce the surface velocity below the first critical point. The significance of vegetation in causing deposition has already been pointed out, the important element being the fact that grasses, etc., project above the surface and so check the wind's velocity. On erosional slopes the sand is protected by somewhat scattered grasses rather than by a continuous mat or blanket. In the absence of such a blanket the sand of course lies at its angle of rest. Such is the case along most of the shore face where the waves are cutting back the beach.

The presence of vegetation is of very large significance in the dunes, since without it the entire area would be a great sand waste such as is found in arid deserts.

THE MOVEMENT OF DUNES

NATURE

As already pointed out, sand is moved by the wind either by a combination of rolling and short jumps, as in the migration of ripples, or by being blown in sheets. The mass movement of dunes is now to be considered. It has often been suggested that dunes are waves of sand, not merely superficially, but in their mode of movement and characteristics. It is only in a very limited sense, however, that sand may be considered even as a semifluid. It can be poured, but it has no cohesion, capillarity, diffusion, or surface tension; and, more important still, the action of gravity on sand is quite different from that on a fluid. The advance of a dune does not consist in a disturbance passing through a medium, and there is no orbital movement of the particles. Instead, the migration of a dune is due to the erosion of the windward face, the transportation of this sand, together possibly with that from the beach up the slope, and the accumulation of this material on the lee side. Dune movement is thus best understood, not by a comparison with water waves, but as the aggregate movement resulting from the change in position of the individual grains of sand.

Many dune authorities have written of the importance of the wind eddy, formed in the lee of both ripples and dunes, in steepening the lee slope and checking advance. Cornish, for example, has frequently emphasized

its importance, saying that the lee slope is not due to the sand rolling to
the angle of rest, but to undercutting by the lee eddy. During the three
years of field work involved in the preparation of this report, visits to the
dune country under all conditions of movement have failed to reveal evidence in support of this theory. Wherever the wind has been carrying
sand over the blowout, the lee slope is unstable and is as steep as the sand
will lie. Blowouts often advance into forests where no eddy could be operative, yet the same 32° angle is present from the top to the bottom of the
lee slope (Plate XVII, *b*). Plate XVII, *a*, illustrates a very exceptional
crescentic dune formed under the lee of a larger dune to the left, where the
eddy is of importance in producing the knife-edge crest. Such forms are
quite rare in this area.

RATE

Other conditions remaining constant, dunes having longer windward
slopes will move more slowly than similar but smaller ones because of the
larger amount of sand to be carried up to the crests. This leads to the following general law of dune movement as formulated by Konschin: *The
velocity of dune movement is directly proportional to the speed of the wind and
inversely to the mass of the dune.*[1] This principle, or the recognition of it,
has been largely overlooked in the literature, and the failure to appreciate
its significance has introduced many fallacies. It is at once apparent that
the larger the dune, the more slowly it will move. Thus in any one dune if
one portion is lower, that is, if the mass of that part is less than other parts
of the dune, it will move more rapidly. The movement may be thought of
likewise in terms of the area of the cross-sections. Where an isolated hill
transverse to the wind is subject to migration, the lower extremities advance more rapidly than the summit and develop into the horns of a cres-
cent, the whole forming the crescentic or barchan dunes found in many
deserts, but only rarely produced in the Indiana complex. Figure 3 illustrates the relation between mass and rate of movement, the rate remaining
constant with uniform mass but accelerating when the mass is decreased
and retarding when the mass increases.

In any region of variable winds the advance of a dune is frequently
checked or reversed. Where the winds are so widely distributed from all
points of the compass as in this area, they are a limiting factor of much importance. The check may thus be sufficient sometimes to prevent net
movement entirely, only the upper layers being shifted from side to side,

---

[1] Quoted by Sven Hedin: "Scientific Results of a Journey in Central Asia,"
(Stockholm, Lithographic Institute, 1904), II, 403.

while the main mass remains stationary (Fig. 4). From early maps of caravan routes and records of oases, certain dunes in the Sahara are known not to have moved appreciably for centuries.

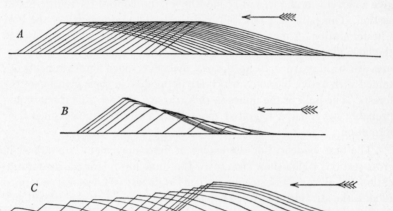

FIG. 3.—The relation between mass and velocity. *A*, a dune advancing with the same speed because the mass remains the same. *B*, a dune advancing more slowly as the mass increases. *C*, a dune advancing more rapidly as the mass decreases. After Sven Hedin.

FIG. 4.—The stability of dunes despite shifting winds. The surface sand is moved to and fro by the wind, but the bulk of the dune remains unaffected. The departure of the lines from a radial direction indicates the relative movement. After Sven Hedin.

EXTENT

Numerous measurements have been made of the rate of dune advance in various parts of the world, but in the absence of data as to the size of the dunes they are of little value. The following are typical: Baltic coastal dunes, 18 feet per year; Gascony, 20–25 meters per year; Libyan Desert, 10–20 meters per year; Ismailia, $\frac{3}{4}$ inch per hour.[1] Helman found a dune advance in China of 4.30 meters per year with a movement of 75 cubic meters of sand to the running meter of the length of the dune.[2] In the

[1] H. J. L. Beadnell, "Sand Dunes of the Libyan Desert," *Geographical Journal*, XXXV (1910), 379.

[2] Pehr Olsson-Seffer, "The Genesis and Development of Sand Formations on Marine Coasts," *Augustana Library Publication No. 7* (1910), p. 26.

Indiana dunes Hardesty and Fulton found an advance of 5 feet in four months near Dune Park, and Cowles measured 10 feet in six months.[1] Measurements by the writer on the large blowout north of Port Chester give a movement of 3 feet in 11 months for the slope of the southernmost section. This point is $\frac{1}{4}$ mile south of the lake and due north of the Port Chester station. A measurement on the eastern sector, which is closer to the lake, gives a lee advance of $1\frac{1}{2}$ feet in the same interval. These figures are for May, 1922, to April, 1923, inclusive. Such figures are only obtained with active blowouts which are impressive in their invasion of the forests. The bulk of the dunes in this area are at present stationary and probably never have migrated more than a short distance since their formation.

The best evidence for the extent of dune movement is obtained in cross-sections which show structure. If a dune has migrated, the stratification will all consist of steeply dipping lee slopes; whereas if it is formed *in situ*, the stratification will be roughly concentric with the present surface. Two cross-sections offer important evidence on this point. North of Johnsfield a drainage channel has been cut across the muck flat and through the dunes. In the center of the flat the muck is more than 4 feet thick, but adjacent to the dunes it thins to a few inches. In the center of Plate XVIII, *b*, may be seen a dark line which marks the continuation of the muck, and overlying it is the lee stratification of the southernmost dune of the complex. This zone of lee structure is only about 200 feet wide, and beyond it the muck horizon entirely disappears. It has often been supposed that all the dunes have migrated from the present shore; but if this were the case there would not be the abrupt pinching out of the muck horizon, and the lee structure would be more extensive. The second cross-section is north of Long Lake, where the Inland Steel Company is cutting away the dunes (Fig. 5). Here the stratification of the southernmost ridge is very largely concentric with the surface and there can have been but very little migration. Lee structure is of course seen in fossil blowouts, but with former fore dune ridges it is largely subordinate. The muck underlying the lake does not continue under the dunes. The interpretation placed upon this evidence is that, as the level of the glacial lakes was lowered, the shore receded and, since the slope of the lake bottom near shore was gentle, offshore bars were built up which developed above the water and became the site of fore dune ridges. The areas behind these new beaches formed lagoons and have now become muck land. The

---

[1] Rollin D. Salisbury and William C. Alden, "The Geography of Chicago and Its Environs," *Geographic Society of Chicago Bull. No. 1*, revised ed. (1920), p. 58.

widening of the beach has resulted in the development of new fore dunes farther and farther lakeward.

Active blowout dunes are such striking features and move so rapidly during their lifetime that the impression of constant change is applied to all the dunes. In extent, however, they involve but 1 or 2 per cent of the entire area and are not to be regarded as typical of the other relatively stable dune forms. Further, it seems probable that blowouts are much more common today than previously.

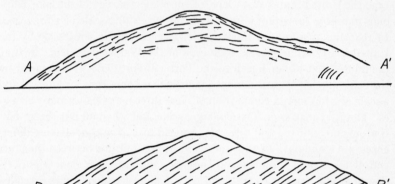

FIG. 5. *A–A'*, cross-section of fore dune ridge, immediately north of Long Lake. *B–B'*, stratification as it would appear in a dune which has migrated.

THE CHANGING POSITION OF THE SHORE LINE

The evidence here presented indicates that the development of the Indiana dunes has taken place largely through the continued widening of the beach and the formation of successive fore dune ridges, rather than that all dunes of the complex are related to the present shore. There seems reason to believe that conditions now operative in bringing sand to the head of the lake for dune formation have been dominant in the past. Thus, in the area where the dunes are now being built the complex is widest, and the interior beach lines are most distant from the lake. While the dune area is being widened at the expense of the lake in the Miller area, to the east the lake is actively cutting back the dunes, especially around Michigan City. The evidence of this erosion is found in the character of the shore. In place of the typical fore dune characteristics the mature established dunes are directly along the shore face, which is quite steep and often strewn with undermined trees. The beach is narrow and the subaqueous accumulation of sand small. Where the waves are cutting into a fore dune ridge, but little sand is blown up the steep erosion slope inland, except in blowouts. Where the ridges are low or poorly developed, the sand may be blown inland in a continuous belt resembling a very wide irregular blowout. Such is the case between Michigan City and the Johnsfield Creek.

Around the head of the lake direct evidence is available as to the rate of the widening of the beach and the consequent filling in of the lake. In 1870 the United States War Department made a survey of the lake, mapping the shore topography in 10-foot contours and a scale of 1 to 20,000. In 1910 the area around Gary was resurveyed on the same scale by the United States Lake Survey, a division of the War Department. In 1921 the dunes from Miller Beach to the Porter County line were mapped by the Gary municipal park commissioners with a 2-foot contour interval and a scale of 1 to 1200. A comparison of these three maps shows many changes. The 1921 map is on a much larger scale, but when all but the 10-foot contours are omitted and the scale changed to 1 to 20,000, striking differences still stand out. In 1870 there was no contour line between the blind end of the Grand Calumet and the lake, and the river doubtless overflowed at high water. In 1910 and 1921, a belt of 50-foot dunes extended across this location. In much of the region it is possible only approximately to correlate positions; but not only is the same fore dune ridge present on all maps, though slightly higher at present, but the higher interior ridges as well are apparent. One of the most stable points is a sharp turn in the south bank of the Grand Calumet east of Miller Beach. This is now well wooded and apparently no extensive change has taken place since 1870. An examination of the maps shows it to be 725 feet from the shore in 1870, 1,025 feet in 1910, and 1,050 feet on the 1921 map. Since the 1870 and 1910 maps were made on the same scale and standard of accuracy, they perhaps offer the best evidence as to the rate of filling, namely, an average of 7.5 feet per year. Such changes are only to be considered in terms of a long period of years, for individual seasons or decades might show greatly varying and even reversed figures.

Another line of evidence as to the relation between deposition in the vicinity of Miller and erosion farther east has been furnished by Professor H. C. Cowles, of the University of Chicago.[1] The normal ecological sequence inland is (1) the beach, (2) the fore dune association with the cottonwoods, (3) the oaks, and (4) the pines. Around Miller this order is nor-

[1] Personal communication.

mal, but at progressive locations to the east, the cottonwoods largely drop out, and the oaks and finally the pines come directly up to the shore face, giving the dunes a much more mature aspect. Since pines never develop in areas of shifting sands near the beach, it appears that the zone of cottonwoods and oaks has been removed by erosion, and that the beach at one time was much farther to the north.

CHAPTER V

HISTORICAL GEOLOGY

THE RETREAT OF THE LATE WISCONSIN ICE

At its maximum the Lake Michigan lobe of the late Wisconsin ice-sheet extended southward, slightly beyond Indianapolis, to about the middle of Indiana. During its retreat from this maximum stage, recessional moraines were deposited at the margin of the ice whenever that margin remained stationary for any considerable length of time. The most important of these moraines for this area is the Valparaiso Moraine, which is roughly concentric with the shore of Lake Michigan. Between it and the lake are smaller moraine ridges which mark lesser halts of the ice front. The entire recessional history of the ice was characterized by variations in the position of the ice front, and Taylor states that in all probability the retreating ice here went through the same series of oscillations, with strongly marked retreats and advances, which took place in the Huron-Erie basin. The evidence of these oscillations, however, is not generally so well marked around the head of Lake Michigan. An interpretation of the chronology in terms of climatic fluctuations would no doubt furnish much light on these oscillations.

No direct evidence has been obtained as to the length of time since the formation of the Valparaiso Moraine. In the absence of such information we may accept the representative figure of 25,000 years since the maximum stage of the late Wisconsin ice. Recent work by Antevs on the ice lobe which occupied the Connecticut Valley gives exact figures for the rate of recession of the ice front there. Through study of the seasonal clay layers, or varves, deposited in lakes at the ice front, he has been able to locate the ice margin year by year. The area which he has investigated in this manner extends from Hartford, Connecticut, to St. Johnsbury, Vermont, a distance of 185 miles. The time occupied by the recession of the ice front across this strip was 4,100 years, an average of 22 years to the mile, or 238 feet per year. If the rate of recession for Lake Michigan was of the same order of magnitude, about 7,150 years would be required for the ice front to melt back from the Valparaiso Moraine to the Strait of Mackinac. Allowing for the ice recession and adjustment of elevations in the St. Lawrence region, it seems probable that the pre–Lake Michigan lacustrine stages did not together exceed 10,000 years.

CHANGES IN LAKE LEVEL

While the margin of the Lake Michigan lobe stood on the Valparaiso Moraine, the water from the melting ice flowed to the south. As the edge of the ice receded north of the Valparaiso divide, the water from the melting ice formed a lake between the glacier on the north and the terminal or ground moraine to the south. From the record of beach lines and lake flats we know that the level of this lake did not remain constant, but that there were several stages of water level.

The great weight of the ice during the stage of glaciation has been thought to have depressed this entire region. Following the removal of the load by melting, the surface of the region only gradually returned to its present level, and this graded uplift was naturally greatest to the north, where the ice had been thickest and the load greatest. Thus the earlier beach lines which were originally horizontal are now tilted, in some cases departing several feet per mile from horizontality. This tilting has been greatest in the northern part of the Lake Michigan basin. The southern portion seems to have been very slightly warped, presumably because of the shorter length of time during which it was ice-covered and because of the relative thinness of the ice.

The controlling factor in the water-level near the south end of the lake was the outlet through the present course of the Des Plaines River southwest of Chicago, known as the Chicago outlet. Originally the elevation of this channel was more than 60 feet above present lake level. Since then the channel has been cut down till it is now but 8 feet above the present lake level. This channel has been cut in part through limestone strata, and it is thought that harder layers in this limestone may have eroded very slowly, holding the level of the lake nearly stationary at these elevations for considerable periods of time.

No detailed study has been given to possible northern outlets for the lake, but the various outlets suggested include drainage to the west through Green Bay to the Wisconsin River and the Mississippi, drainage to the east through various lower elevations in Michigan, and the present northern outlet. Before correlation of any stage of the lake can be established with any particular northern outlet, the position of the ice front and the relative elevation of the outlet must be determined for that particular time. Further details will be considered under the appropriate stages.

Another possible explanation for changes in lake level lies in the fluctuation of the glacial lobe. It is now known that the ice margin advanced and retreated several times in other areas, and at least one readvance is established in the Michigan basin. Such changes are fundamentally climatic and may be of some importance in the changes of level about to be discussed.

STAGES OF THE LAKE

The name of Lake Chicago has been given by Leverett[1] to the various stages of the ancestral Lake Michigan. It was originally supposed that the history of Lake Chicago was confined to the Lake Michigan basin, but it is now known that several of the stages embraced larger areas, and that the glacial lakes Algonquin and Nipissing are probably represented in Indiana. While the term "Lake Chicago" was originally defined to cover only the body of water emptying through the Chicago outlet, it seems best to broaden its usage to include all pre–Lake Michigan stages of this area—at least until such time as final correlations become established.

SUMMARY

The first appearance of the lake was at the inner margin of the Valparaiso Moraine. The outline of the lake at this stage was roughly crescentic. Drainage was through gaps in the moraine, and the lake at this level is here termed the Valparaiso stage.

The water then dropped to 60 feet above the present mean lake level (578 feet), and shortly after to 55 feet, forming the Glenwood stage. In some places the Glenwood beach is distinctly marked by having cut against the moraine or having built low dunes; for the most part, however, it is poorly defined. Where the original slope of the ground was gentle the water was too shallow for effective wave work on the shore.

Following the Glenwood stage came the Bowmanville low-level stage, when the water apparently fell to about the present lake level. The cause for this low level is not well known, but apparently it was due to the uncovering of a low channel by the retreat of the ice to the north, possibly together with tilting or warping. This outlet may have been through Green Bay to the Wisconsin River.

The next stage is the Calumet, when the lake level rose to 35 feet above the present surface, due to readvance of the ice and warping. The Calumet beaches are usually quite well defined, indicating that the water must have remained at this elevation for a considerable period. Sand dunes were developed along most of the shore, while behind them there is commonly a low strip of land, now drained, but formerly a lagoon or marsh. The shore line is much straighter than the Glenwood beach and in this area is more often wave-built than cut.

[1] Frank Leverett, "Pleistocene Features and Deposits of the Chicago Area," *Chicago Academy of Science, Bull. 2* (May 1897), p. 64.

The Tolleston beach is about 20 feet above the present lake level, and the lowering from the Calumet level was probably due to the cutting down of the Chicago outlet. The beach, dunes, and inclosed marshy tracts are somewhat more complicated than those of the Calumet. Prior to the Tolleston stage the development of Lake Chicago was confined to the local body of water which occupied the Michigan basin. Similar bodies of water were formed in other portions of the Great Lakes region. As the ice sheet gradually melted back to the northeast, ponded waters in the Superior, Huron, and Michigan basins all united to form Lake Algonquin. The Tolleston stage is a part of the early history of Lake Algonquin, and the drainage was via Chicago.

The next change was the lowering of the water to the Sag low-water stage, due to the drainage of Lake Algonquin by Glacial Lake Iroquois through the Trent River Valley, in Ontario, which was at this time uncovered by the ice. This was the Kirkfield stage of Lake Algonquin.

Following this low-water stage, which probably was as low as the present lake level, differential uplift took place in the region of the Trent Valley and the water level was again raised until it overflowed through the Chicago outlet at the Sag and later also through the St. Clair outlet in Michigan. This stage is called the Hammond, and the water rose to about 20 feet above the present surface. This is essentially the same level as that of the Tolleston beach, and no differentiation between the Tolleston and the Hammond stages has been made in the mapping of this area.

Two other stages complete the history of Lake Chicago. The first is a low-water stage related to the recession of the ice to the northeast and is named the North Bay stage. The second is the Englewood stage, with the water level at 12 feet above the present surface. It was due to continued uplift in the areas which had been depressed below sea-level by the ice sheet, and to the consequent shifting of the drainage to the St. Clair and Chicago outlets. With the cutting of the former channel, the level was gradually lowered to that of the present and Lake Chicago became Lake Michigan.

In Indiana and elsewhere the only stages which are well marked by beach lines are the Glenwood, Calumet, and Tolleston-Hammond. Only these three have been given detailed study in the field and they alone are shown on the base map.

VALPARAISO STAGE

The Valparaiso or earliest stage of Lake Chicago has not heretofore been set apart as a distinct stage. It is very largely confined to the state of Indiana and came to an end when the ice margin uncovered the Chicago outlet. In Indiana the Valparaiso Moraine constitutes the divide between the Great Lakes and the Mississippi River drainage. As the ice retreated from this moraine, the irregular depressions between the ice front on one side and the crest of the moraine on the other became filled with water. At first these lakes were isolated, but with further recessions of the ice they coalesced and a narrow and irregularly crescentic lake came into existence. This lake was short lived and no definite beaches were developed; its existence is recorded only by water-laid silts and sands and by the flat surface developed through the subaqueous deposition of the glacial débris. The level of the water probably was not constant, and drainage was through the lower gaps in the moraine as they were successively available. Two such channels are the great gap west of Valparaiso and the one followed by the Baltimore & Ohio Railroad across the divide east of Woodville.

In Indiana the lacustrine plain of the Valparaiso stage is shown south of Dyer and Schererville, in a belt about half a mile wide south of the Lincoln Highway. Eastward to Ainsworth it fingers up into the moraine and merges with the flat of the Glenwood stage to the north. The water covered the margins of the moraine ridge which extends north from Wheeler, especially on the western side. Around the Chesterton embayment the southern margin of the plain comes rather abruptly to the moraine, but to the north it is difficult to separate it from the Glenwood flat, which, because of the shallowness of the water, left a very weak beach. Part of the marsh land within the moraine ridges south and east of Furnessville may belong to the Valparaiso stage. In La Porte County this stage of the lake is represented by rolling sand deposits. It is best shown southeast of Michigan City, along the Galena River and the east and west forks of Trail Creek. This portion of the Valparaiso lake stage was between the main Valparaiso Moraine and Covert Ridge of the lake border moraine. Similar deposits also exist along the western flanks of the latter moraine belt. Drainage was to the west into the Chesterton embayment; and by the time the ice had receded from the lake border moraines in this area, the Sag outlet was doubtless uncovered. The elevation of the water surface was here, apparently, at least 670 feet.

GLENWOOD STAGE

GENERAL DESCRIPTION

As the edge of the ice retreated from the Valparaiso Moraine west of Chicago, another low portion of the moraine was exposed and the ponded waters spilled westward through it. This route is now occupied by the

Des Plaines River and the Chicago Drainage Canal. At first the water-level was about 60 feet above the present surface of Lake Michigan; but, with erosion of the outlet channel, the water shortly fell to 55 feet, or 636 feet above sea-level. This stage of the lake is named from the village of Glenwood, Illinois, near the Indiana boundary, where the beach is well developed. The northward extent of the lake at this stage is unknown, but it probably filled less than half of the Lake Michigan basin at its maximum, and at first was very much smaller. Where the shore line was regular and the water deep enough just off shore, wave action produced a well-defined beach. In protected embayments, however, shoal water prevented effective wave action, so that the beach in such locations is seldom more than 3 feet high. Over large tracts near the shore the depth of the water probably did not exceed 4 or 5 feet. Under such conditions off-shore bars developed and in places they were built above the level of the water by storm waves and became the site of dune accumulations. In many places such ridges are more conspicuous than the true border of the lake. No satisfactory evidences of life in the waters of the lake at this stage have been found. This was doubtless because of the proximity of the ice sheet and the consequent low temperature. There probably was very little vegetation along the shore, but the mastodon and mammoth apparently wandered along the beach, for their remains have been found in Illinois in gravel deposits as old as the Glenwood beach.

AREAL

The beach at Dyer, Indiana, is a very well defined wave-built feature. It averages about 10 feet high, and its width is from 500 to 700 feet. Its slope therefore is gentle. To the north the beach grades down into a clay and loam flat which extends northward $4\frac{1}{2}$ miles to the Calumet beach. East of Dyer, the Lincoln Highway runs along the upper part of the beach for 2 miles, and is at the foot of sand dunes which are from 10 to 30 feet high. Near Dyer the dunes are confined to a narrow strip a few hundred yards wide, but about a mile and a half west of Schererville the dune-covered area is nearly half a mile in width and is more rolling. The Lincoln Highway is here on top of the dunes, which are 30–50 feet above the beach. A mile west of Schererville there is a small gravel pit in the shingle of the beach. Beach pebbles are common all along the former shore. A mile east of Schererville the beach and dunes turn slightly to the north and the beach is here 900 to 1,000 feet wide. In another mile both largely disappear.

West of Hobart there was an island about 6 miles long from northeast to southwest, known as Hobart Island. The water surrounding it was rather shallow, so that currents were checked and sand bars constructed. In part these subaqueous accumulations were built above the water surface by wave action and, with a continued supply of sand, dunes were constructed. Those bars which were not so elevated were doubtless later worked over by the wind when the level of the water was lowered and the area exposed to the atmosphere. Such sand accumulations are found west and north of Hobart Island, and extend from Griffith to New Chicago. Several lines are mapped, but there are numerous smaller patches of sand, especially in the triangle between Griffith, Schererville, and Glen Park.

Hobart Island averages about a mile in width. It is a morainic ridge and stands well above the surrounding plain. The highest point on the Elgin, Joliet & Eastern Railroad is in the center of the island, where the top of the rail reaches 658 feet, more than 20 feet above the Glenwood beach. In general the margin of the island is clearly defined and the lake flat is separated from the typical topography of the terminal moraine by a 3–5-foot cut bank. Due to the protection of the off-shore bars to the northwest, this portion of the island is least clearly set off. The north-eastern tip of the island is a mile and a half northwest of Hobart and the island is here lower. The more irregular topography extends from a mile and a half due west of Hobart to a mile and three-quarters southeast of Ross.

East of Schererville the actual shore of the lake at the Glenwood stage is less distinct. There are a few beaches 3 feet high, but under the protection of Hobart Island they are seldom distinct. With the lowering of the Chicago outlet the actual position of the shore line doubtless changed. The beach is near the intersection of the Chesapeake & Ohio and the Gary & Southern railways. At Merrilville it is six-tenths of a mile north of the Lincoln Highway, and 2 miles farther east it is seven-tenths of a mile north of the Highway. For the next mile and a half it is quite irregular, swinging slightly to the south. At Ainsworth the beach is half a mile north of the Grand Trunk Railway, and swings to the south of the railway where the latter crosses Deep River. In this region, and likewise in Porter County, where the actual beach is obscure, reliance has been placed on the soil maps of the Bureau of Soils. On these maps it is possible to differentiate water-laid from ice-laid soils and very valuable information has thus been derived.

The Glenwood beach, on the western edge of Porter County, is seven-tenths of a mile north of the Grand Trunk Railway and trends south of east for a mile, where it turns to the north and follows the moraine which extends north of Wheeler. This ridge is poorly marked, and, while the topography is that of a terminal moraine along the center, it grades into the Glenwood flat along the margins, especially to the west. Probably the Valparaiso lake stage was influential in modifying its borders. The Glenwood beach can be traced northward through the western edge of Wheeler a mile, then northeast for three-quarters of a mile, and then north nearly to the intersection of the Gary and Interurban electric road and the Elgin, Joliet & Eastern Railroad. From here it extends in a southerly direction nearly to the point where the Pennsylvania Railroad crosses Salt Creek. North and west of the tip of the Wheeler morainic extension are numerous rolling sand hills and ridges. In part these are doubtless related to the Glenwood stage, being similar in origin to those described west of Hobart Island, but those north and west of Crisman are probably Calumet in age.

East of Salt Creek the Valparaiso Moraine is comparatively rough and the lake flat meets it abruptly though in an irregular contact. From near the Pennsylvania Railroad the beach extends north-northeast for 3 miles, then east for 2 miles, and north to within a mile of Chesterton. East of Chesterton there was a long bay which extended to the La Porte County line, having an average width of a mile and a half. It is now the course of the Grand Calumet River. In this bay there are many sandy deposits, evidently formed as deltas from streams flowing from the moraine. There is no well defined continuous shore, but in places there are cut banks 3 or 4 feet high. The northern shore of this bay extends east and west and lies about a mile east of Chesterton. It coincides with the southern edge of the lake border moraine, and extends as far as Baileytown, where it turns back to the east, parallel with the lake.

South of Baileytown the beach is clearly marked, but beyond its turn to the east around the end of the moraine ridge it is obscured by the Calumet beach which was formed in the same place. For about two miles eastward the younger Calumet beach and dune belt is strongly defined and has obscured the Glenwood record. Sand dunes veneer the moraine and the point at which the beach lines separate is not known, but south of Tremont and probably south of Port Chester they are separate. From here east to Michigan City the Glenwood shore line is well developed and is backed by low rolling dunes up to 40 feet high. The beach slope is well preserved and beach gravel is common. Southeast of Johnsfield are several small gravel pits. In part the beach is cut against the moraine and the dunes are merely a veneer. The dune sand deposits are about half a mile in width. A mile and a half northeast of Furnessville the beach is crossed by the Michigan Central Railroad. From this point the beach and the railroad are parallel as far as the La Porte–Porter County line. An off-shore bar is well developed beyond Furnessville and the railroad runs along its crest.

At the La Porte–Porter County line the beach is just south of the Pere Marquette Railroad and extends northeast into Michigan City. The Pere Marquette station, the Greenwood Cemetery, and the intersection of Michigan Street and Woodland Avenue mark the course of the beach through the city.

South and east of Michigan City rolling sand hills, in large part merely veneered upon drift, characterize the strip between the Valparaiso and the lake border moraines. This area extends along the east and west forks of Trail Creek, and Leverett states that an arm of the Glenwood Lake occupied the area, connection with the open lake being through the narrow main valley of Trail Creek.[1] However, the profile of the Chicago, Indianapolis & Louisville Railroad gives the lowest elevation in this area as 660 feet, while the Lake Erie & Western Railroad is over 750 feet between the moraines. Only around the junction of the east and west forks does the elevation drop below 636 feet, and this is due to post-glacial erosion.

Leverett later states, however, that "the Trail Creek drainage stands in the line of a small glacial lake that discharged southwestward to the incipient Lake Chicago at Chesterton. Deposits of sand several feet deep along the line of these pools may be in part the deposit of this drainage, and thus antedate the Glenwood beach."[2] They would thus belong to the Valparaiso stage; and if any body of water occupied this area during Glenwood time it had but limited connection with the main lake and is not regarded as a real part thereof.

Beyond Michigan City the beach swings east of the Pere Marquette Railroad, the two then running parallel about half a mile apart into Michigan. The beach is here indistinct, and rolling sand hills are found between it and the Lake Border Moraine. The Michigan line crosses the Glenwood beach 3 miles east of the lake.

BOWMANVILLE STAGE

The question of a low-level stage following the Glenwood has been much discussed for many years. It was originally proposed by Andrews,

[1] Frank Leverett, "The Illinois Glacial Lobe," *U.S. Geological Survey Monograph 38* (1899), p. 432.

[2] Frank Leverett and Frank Taylor, "The Pleistocene of Indiana and Michigan," *U.S. Geological Survey Monograph 53* (1915), p. 351.

who discovered a widespread silt and peat deposit lying on Glenwood sand, or upon the till, and beneath the Calumet Beach deposits.[1] This deposit is especially well exposed around Evanston; and while it has been suggested that the overlying sand is merely a bar built out over the silt during the Glenwood stage, its extensive distribution in various areas renders this improbable. More recently Baker[2] has discovered similar and more striking evidence at Bowmanville, Illinois, and elsewhere. The Glenwood and Calumet beaches are 55 feet and 35 feet above the lake, and these peat deposits extend to within a few feet of the present lake surface. Thus they record a marshy land surface below the Calumet level before that shore line was formed. This definitely indicates a low-water stage.

In the dune area between Michigan City and the creek which enters the lake north of Johnsfield, there are numerous outcrops of a compact bluish-green clay, filled with shells and woody tissue. This occurrence has been noted by other writers, but its significance has commonly been overlooked. Plate XIX, *b*, shows the westernmost exposure, Johnsfield Creek being seen in the foreground. The section is as follows:

		Thickness (Inches)
11	Recent dune sand	+36
10	Bluish-green clay shale	12
9	Sand, topset bedding at 20° max	30
8	Sand, foreset bedding	10
7	Sand, bottomest bedding	10
6	Not exposed	10
5	Shaly sand	4
4	Not exposed	12
3	Hard stiff blue-green clay-shale	4
2	Sand	12
1	Present lake level	

Both clay horizons are compact, the formation being so dense and resistant that it forms bowlders on the beach. The lower clay is harder and somewhat less calcareous than the upper, although both effervesce vigorously in dilute hydrochloric acid. The iron is in the ferrous condition, suggesting deposition under water. The abundance of vegetable remains seems to indicate that these layers were deposited in shallow marshes as

[1] Edmund Andrews, "The North American Lakes Considered as Chronometers of Post-Glacial Time," *Trans. Chicago Academy of Science*, II (1870), p. 14.

[2] Frank C. Baker, "The Life of Glacial Lake Chicago," *Science*, new series, XXXI (1910), 715.

a combination of shell marl and peat. The cross-bedding of the sand, largely free from pebbles, presents a peculiar problem, since the lake is 50 yards to the left of the exposure of which the view is taken looking east. This bedding is typical of delta structure, but it could not have been formed by a stream flowing north into the lake. The only explanation is that it represents material washed over the landward side of a bar which stood to the north, and that this bar migrated landward, eventually covering the lower clay.

Mr. Frank C. Baker has kindly examined shells from these marls and reports that the following species are represented: *Planorbis deflectus* Say, *Amnicola limosa* Say, *Pisidium*, fragments. These forms were abundant during the earlier stages of the lake and may or may not represent the Bowmanville stage.

Toward Michigan City the upper clay comes within 2 feet of the lake level and the lower layer is not exposed. About a mile east of Johnsfield Creek the waves are actively cutting into the dunes and there is a nearly vertical face in the old sand at the inner margin of the beach. Plate XIX, *a*, shows the upper clay layer at the edge of the beach. Its base is 6 feet above the lake and its top grades up into sandy clay at 8 feet. Above this is eolian cross-bedded sand, marked in the illustration by the trowel. At the top of the exposure may be seen beach pebbles which cover a large flat area back from the shore. Those shown here are 15 feet above Lake Michigan, but they have slumped somewhat, their original position having been about 20 feet above the present lake.

These pebbles mark the position of the Tolleston-Hammond shore line and it is here that the beach runs out into Lake Michigan. There can be no question about the eolian nature of the cross-bedding, for it is exposed continuously. The section in Plate XIX, *a*, is a few feet from that in Plate XIX, *b*. Because of the impervious nature of the clay, water seeps out above it and its stratification is obscured; the tangential bedding of the sand, however, is easily traced to within 6 or 8 inches of the upper limit of the clay. Since there seems to be no clear indication anywhere of low water between the Calumet and Tolleston stages, this evidence of a land surface must be related either to the Bowmanville or to the Sag low-water stage. If this clay horizon is of the age assigned, it seems probable that, by the time of the Sag stage, it would be covered by lake silt and sand to the extent of several feet. Furthermore, the deposition of the Tolleston beach would have still further buried it so that dunes could scarcely be formed in such a location during the Sag stage. It seems probable, therefore, that the eolian cross-bedding dates from the Bowmanville stage, either being built on a barrier beach over the clay, or being formed during a somewhat lower part of the stage.

While the existence of a Bowmanville stage appears probable on the basis of the depositional evidence, the most serious objection relates to an outlet for the lake. Even though the ice should have retreated sufficiently to clear the Strait of Mackinac, the other glacial lakes at this time do not seem to have had sufficiently low levels to allow Lake Chicago to fall 55 feet. Upham has suggested that the drainage at this time was by way of Green Bay and Portage to the Wisconsin and Mississippi rivers.[1] This is the lowest outlet between Chicago and the *col* of the St. Croix River near the north end of the lake. The elevation of the Portage outlet is now 200 feet above the Chicago outlet, but it is entirely possible that warping may have given it this elevation subsequent to the Bowmanville stage. Alden has discovered evidence for a readvance of the ice near Milwaukee, and it may be that the Portage outlet was open during the time of the maximum recession and was closed by this readvance. Alden does not accept Upham's suggestion.[2] It may be possible that the Bowmanville represents an intermediate stage during Glenwood time rather than a subsequent stage. The life of this stage was varied and abundant.

Further evidence concerning the time and extent of the Bowmanville interval of emergence is desired, together with more precise knowledge as to the outlet.

CALUMET STAGE

GENERAL

During the Calumet stage of Lake Chicago the water surface was 35–40 feet above the present level, or 20 feet below the Glenwood stage. The Calumet beach is in most places well defined and it seems probable that the water stood at this level for an extended period, much longer than the duration of the Glenwood stage. Drainage was by way of the Chicago outlet, and it appears that a bed of hard rock there must have offered such resistance that considerable time was required to erode it. It is improbable that there was a waterfall at the Sag, but there may have been a series of rapids. On the whole, the Calumet beach is characterized by larger deposits of sand and gravel than the Glenwood, and cut banks are less conspicuous. Dune accumulations are extensive, many dunes reaching 40 feet in height. The beach is best preserved along the southern side of the

[1] Warren Upham, "Glacial Lake Nicolet," *American Geologist*, Vol. XXXII (1903), 105–15.

[2] William C. Alden, "The Quaternary Geology of Southeastern Wisconsin," *U.S. Geological Survey Professional Paper 106* (1918), p. 325.

Little Calumet River, in Lake County, in consequence of which the name Calumet has been given to it.

No conclusive evidences of life in the waters of this stage have been reported from its beach deposits. Apparently the rising waters from the Bowmanville stage exterminated much of the biota of that stage, covering it with sand and gravel. But inasmuch as evidences of aquatic life are rather uncommon even on the present shore, one should not conclude that the waters of the lake were lifeless at this time, especially in view of the abundant evidence found in the Tolleston beach.

AREAL

In Lake County the Calumet beach is easily traced along the Ridge Road from Munster to Glen Park. Along the state line it is ten miles south of the lake and a mile from the Little Calumet River. The course of the beach across the county is a broad smooth arc with none of the irregularities found in the Glenwood beach. The beach itself is broad and slopes gently to the north, while dunes flank it to the south. In the eastern five miles of the county the dunes are confined to a narrow ridge a few hundred yards wide. North of Griffith they broaden to half a mile and continue at this or a somewhat greater width across the eastern part of the county. East of Glen Park the dune ridges built up during the Glenwood stage merge with those of the Calumet beach and there is considerable irregularity in the dune belt. From a point a mile east of Glen Park to and beyond Deep River, the Michigan Central Railroad runs near the beach. At East Gary this railroad crosses the beach close to the county line.

Off-shore bars are commonly associated with the Calumet beach in Lake County, there being an almost continuous bar from Munster to Deep River. Due to accumulation of sand by both waves and wind, the beach and dunes constitute a continuous ridge, and the plain to the south is therefore poorly drained. This plain was the bed of the lake during the Glenwood stage and is now largely covered by muck and clay soils. Before drainage that portion north and west of Griffith was known as the Cady Marsh, and peat was cut here for some years.

Around Hobart is a deposit of heavy lake clay covering an area approximately 2 miles east and west by 4 miles north and south and used extensively for brick and tile. This clay is calcareous and contains many small calcareous concretions at the base of the leached zone, about 5 feet below the surface. The pit of the National Fire Proofing Company at Hobart is 50 feet deep and the upper 15 feet is yellowish. This upper clay has sandy partings which average ⅛ inch in thickness, while the clay layers average 6 inches. The next 35 feet is composed of dense bluish clay with thinner beds and less sand. The layers average about one inch in thickness. At the base of the main pit is a pebble horizon, and below it, for at least 30 feet, the clay is reported to be impure, presumably being glacial drift rather than lake sediment. These layers represent seasonal deposition similar to that observed by Antevs in New England and elsewhere. During the spring and summer sand and silt were washed into the basin. The sand settled rapidly, but the finer particles of clay remained in suspension and only settled out during the winter when the water was quiet and little sediment was being brought by the streams. Thus an annual layer, or varve, is composed of a lower coarse sandy portion grading up to finer clay. Under ideal conditions the thicknesses of these varves are rough indexes of the summer temperature and melting, but around Hobart they were influenced by other factors and are therefore quite irregular. The total number of years represented in the exposure is between 400 and 500. Somewhat similar clays are found in the valley of Salt Creek and between Munster and Dyer. In the latter location they are extensively used for brick making.

The Porter–Lake County line crosses the Calumet beach three miles south of Lake Michigan. The beach has a regular course as far as Salt Creek. Around Crissman the dunes are more rolling and overlap the sand of the Glenwood stage, the two together having a width of about 2 miles. The extent to which the Calumet stage of Lake Chicago entered the embayment southeast of Dune Park is not known. The land is nearly level and the lake probably ended in a marsh rather than with a definite beach. In the absence of a topographic map no precise line has been drawn. Presumably the water extended a considerable distance up the Salt Creek and Little Calumet valleys; but it seems doubtful whether much more of the embayment was flooded. Along the western side of Salt Creek the shore line is developed to and beyond McCool.

East of Baileytown the beach is also very well developed and is fully as distinct as in Lake County. It parallels the Chicago, Lake Shore & South Bend Electric Railway, which runs along the lower part of the beach to Johnsfield. Around Baileytown and Port Chester there are patches of the moraine parallel to the beach, but elsewhere it is generally obscured by dune sand. The dune belt is commonly a quarter to half a mile wide, and in the west is merely a veneer on the moraine which can be seen along the southern margin of the dunes. The beach is straight and broad and is commonly without off-shore bars. To the north of the beach is a belt of marsh and muck more than half a mile wide which can be crossed only on the few roads. This marsh lies along the southern margin of the main dune complex. This beach has sometimes been mistaken for that of the Tolleston, but the present work definitely fixes it as Calumet in age. Elevations from the profiles of the new Dunes Highway and the Chicago, Lake Shore & South Bend Electric Railway show the beach elevation to be everywhere between 617 and 620 feet.

The Porter–La Porte County line crosses the beach about a mile south of Lake Michigan. Thence, the beach is recognizable near the Indiana State Penitentiary and is crossed by Franklin Street at Fifth Street, Michigan City. The dunes of the beach are highest along Eleventh Street. Where Trail Creek crosses the old shore line, the latter has been largely destroyed, but a mile northeast of Michigan City it is distinct. It is paralleled by the Michigan Central Railroad to the east and is about half a mile from the lake, where it is separated from the main complex by a strip of low land. The Michigan Central Railroad and the Dunes Highway run on the associated dunes. At the Michigan border the beach is a mile from the present lake.

TOLLESTON STAGE

GENERAL

Following the Calumet stage, the water surface of Lake Chicago fell about 15 feet, and at this level was built the Tolleston beach, 20–25 feet above the present surface of Lake Michigan and about 605 feet above sea-level. There is no definite evidence of a low-level period between the Calumet and Tolleston stages, and the change in elevation apparently was due to the cutting down of the Chicago outlet. The stage is named from the village of Tolleston, now incorporated in the western part of Gary. The beach is generally absent in Michigan and north of Chicago, and in Indiana its location is often obscure. This is due largely to the complex changes in lake level which followed it.

The Tolleston beach, as mapped, is a combination of that produced by the Tolleston and Hammond stages. Since they had nearly the same level, no differentiation seems possible. At this time Lake Chicago was continuous with Lake Algonquin to the northeast and northwest, and the Tolleston stage is equivalent to the initial stage of Lake Algonquin. Everywhere in Indiana the Tolleston beach is built up of sand rather than cut into drift. The depth of sand under the beach is 25 feet in many cases and the known maximum is at Aetna, where it is 40 feet. Dune accumulations are commonly larger than with any of the higher beaches. The beach itself is broad, and off-shore bars are so abundant that the actual beach is often in question.

A rich fauna of mussels lived in the lake, as well as other forms of life. In the beach deposits have been found the bones of birds, mastodons, mammoths, and deer.

AREAL

The Tolleston Beach on the Indiana-Illinois line lies in the southern edge of Hammond, $7\frac{1}{4}$ miles from the lake. It trends southward through the northern part of Hessville, and eastward through the southern edge of Tolleston, into Gary, where it crosses Broadway three blocks north of the Pennsylvania Railroad intersection. Between Gary and Hessville the dune belt is broader and there are several low ridges. These may mark positions of the Tolleston beach before the shore was straightened and the main position established. The beach passes through Aetna and the southern edge of Miller, leaving the county south of Long Lake, one mile from Lake Michigan. East of Gary the dunes of the Tolleston beach are well developed, reaching 50 feet in height, while the belt averages over half a mile in width. They are covered by grasses, shrubs, and a few scrub oaks. In the hollows are numerous patches of muck. Around Long Lake the muck and marsh land is especially extensive and the northern half of the dune belt is largely composed of low ridges, with intervening swales, often filled with water. The exact position of the shore line is quite indefinite, but it seems clearly to be south of Long Lake.

From the vicinity of Long Lake the trend of the Tolleston beach is northeastward. It is crossed by the Chicago, Lake Shore & South Bend Electric Railway half a mile east of the Porter County line. It is one-eighth of a mile north of Wicliffe and over half a mile north of the Dune Park Electric Station. It probably lies south of Warner Lake and Little Lake and is three-fourths of a mile north of Mineral Springs. At Waverly, coarse sand and small beach pebbles have been found four-tenths of a mile from the shore and also along Dune Creek. Here the shingle is composed of fragments up to 4 inches in diameter and is 15 feet above Lake Michigan. East of Waverly the former shore line is half to a quarter of a mile from the present lake and is largely obscured. Apparently the post-Tolleston slope of the lake floor was steeper there than farther west, so that less of a barrier beach with its lagoon-marsh was developed at the next high-water stage.

Between the mouth of the creek north of Johnsfield and the La Porte County line there are numerous exposures along the shore of pebbly sand from 15 to 20 feet above the lake, which represent the shingle of the Tolleston beach. The dunes are being rapidly eroded in this area, and farther east evidence of the Tolleston beach is absent. The former shore line extends out into the lake at about the Porter–La Porte County line.

METHOD OF LOCATION

In Porter County the beach is partially covered by dunes of later age, and even where the actual beach is exposed, it is difficult to recognize. The location of the shore line by ordinary physiographic methods is largely out of the question and all previous maps of this area have been in error in regard to the position of the Tolleston beach. The method by which the position of the beach has been determined may here be mentioned. At the beginning of this study of the Indiana dunes it was assumed that all of the dune sand had been blown inland from something like the present shore. As Salisbury stated, "the sand for all the dunes was derived from the shore, and was driven inland by the winds from the lake. The older dunes (those to the south) have migrated farther than the younger ones." It was therefore anticipated that the sand would show increasing signs of wear with increasing distance from the shore, and the measurement of this wear was the original object of the field work.

In order to examine the effect of wind transportation on the sand grains, nearly fifty samples were gathered along seven lines running back from the lake at right angles from the shore. These samples were passed through a series of sieves and the percentages of four different sizes of grain were computed. On most of the lines the proportion of coarse sand was found to decline back from the shore, while there was a corresponding increase in the finer grades. At a distance varying from one-fourth to one-half mile from the beach, however, a sharp increase in the proportion of coarse sand appeared along several of the lines. This was quite unexpected and field study showed that on the lakeward side of most samples which showed the unexpected coarseness there was an area of muck or marsh. Such patches of low land were often found to be linear, and together they form a more or less continuous belt parallel to the lake. They are well shown on Goodman's Map of the Indiana Dunes, published by the Rand McNally Company. To the north the dunes are higher and steeper, while to the south the topography is smoother.

The suggestion at once arose that this change in the size of the sand indicated a former shore line. The marsh land would therefore correspond to the low country found behind the other beach lines, i.e., a lagoon behind the newly developed barrier beach of the next stage of the lake. A careful search was therefore made for direct evidences of the shore, such as gravel and the actual beach. Both were found in numerous locations and, where elevations are available, they correspond to that of the Tolleston beach, namely, about 605 feet above the sea.

On the basis of the more complete study here presented it seems probable that gradations in size landward are to be accounted for by longer exposure to winds, which shift and wear down the surface sands, and to the addition of finer products of eolian abrasion, picked up from the more active dunes near the shore and veneered over the remainder of the dune complex. Former fore dune ridges and blowouts originally associated with the shore are found preserved in the interior of the area, indicating that relatively little migration has since taken place. If the fore dune ridges were not so closely set, beach gravel would no doubt be found between them; as it is, the shore line evidences are only exposed where they are bordered by the muck or swamp land to the north.

INCLOSED BOGS

Behind the Tolleston beach are extensive areas of muck, with but poor drainage. West of Dune Park the Little Calumet River occupies a broad tract of lowland back of the beach and dune ridge. This tract averages a mile and a half in width and can only be crossed on raised roads. East of Dune Park the dunes of the Tolleston stage are bordered on the south by a belt of muck about half a mile wide, which is commonly marshy (Plate XX, *a*). This muck is commonly 3 or 4 feet thick in the center of the belt. Sand Creek, at Waverly, affords the only natural drainage, but ditches have been dug to the Little Calumet in places and through the dunes to the lake, north of Johnsfield.

Two interesting areas of quaking bog are found in this strip, one just north of Tamarack, on the Chicago, Lake Shore & South Bend Electric Railway, and the other at the southern edge of the dune complex north of Mineral Springs. At this latter locality the bog is roughly 100 feet wide and over 200 yards long. No open pond is exposed, but over the bog there is a mattress of water-soaked vegetation from 4 to 10 inches thick. About thirty tests were made with a pole and in two-thirds of the cases bottom was found at 10 feet. Only two soundings failed to reach bottom at 11 feet. Below the mattress the upper part of the water is dark, but not thick; toward the bottom, however, it commonly is slimy. The bottom itself is distinct, for the pole usually came to a stop within two or three inches after reaching it. On walking over this bog, the vegetation quakes within a ten-foot radius. For the most part it is covered with grasses. In one place, however, there is an isolated clump of tamaracks 25 feet high, below which the water is 10 feet deep (Plate XX, *a*).

When the water-level dropped to the Tolleston stage these bog areas apparently were unfilled depressions, possibly related to irregularities in the original drift surface. Since the Tolleston beach was built up largely as a barrier, all of this muck land was inclosed as a lagoon. Most of the lagoon was shallow, so that with the natural inwash and the encroachment of vegetation it largely became filled. But in these two bog areas the depth was greater and they were not filled with sediment. Instead, floating vegetation grew out from their margins, in time entirely covering the pond and forming a quaking bog. Complete filling of the depression can now take place only by the growth of vegetation, a relatively slow process as measured in years.

SAG LOW-WATER STAGE

Following the Tolleston stage the lake had a second low-water period, called the Sag stage from deposits in the region of the Sag. The water-level fell to about 10 feet above the present lake surface, due to the uncovering of a lower northern outlet by the retreat of the ice. With the melting back of the ice, the Trent River Valley in Ontario was uncovered, and Lake Algonquin (Superior, Huron, and Michigan basins) drained through it into Lake Iroquois, the forerunner of Lake Ontario. The St. Lawrence Valley was still blocked, so that drainage reached the Atlantic by way of the Mohawk and Hudson rivers. This change of outlet caused a lowering of the water in the dune country and the land surface was enlarged. The Chicago outlet was used only to a slight degree, if at all.

While this stage of Lake Chicago is given a local name, it is the equivalent of the Kirkfield stage of Lake Algonquin, so named from the town of Kirkfield along the Trent outlet in Ontario. The direct evidence for this stage is found in Illinois rather than in the dune country. Life during this stage was more abundant than at any earlier stage, seventy-five species and varieties of mollusks, as well as many other forms of life, being known.

HAMMOND STAGE

Differential uplift in the region of the Trent Valley as the great ice sheet continued to retreat eventually raised the elevation of the outlet at Kirkfield until the waters of Lake Algonquin again discharged through the Chicago outlet. The water thus rose approximately to the level of the Tolleston stage, but, due to cutting in the Chicago outlet and partial discharge through the St. Clair River to the Lake Erie basin, the level of the Hammond stage was about 600 feet above the sea, or 20 feet above the present lake surface. The waves of this stage no doubt largely effaced the original Tolleston beach, but the location of the Tolleston and Hammond beaches must have been essentially the same. The Kirkfield and Hammond stages have sometimes been recognized as the Middle and Lower Tolleston, but since this involves an incorrect implication, Baker has given them distinct rank.

It is only within rather recent years that the original Tolleston stage has been thus divided, and as a consequence no large-scale studies of the two beaches have been made. On the areal map of this region they are mapped together as Tolleston-Hammond. The assemblage of life was somewhat less abundant during this period than during the Sag stage.

NORTH BAY STAGE

Following the Hammond stage came a third low-level period, described by Baker but not named by him. It was due to continued recession of the ice until a low pass was uncovered through Lake Nipissing and the Ottawa Valley. The continuous sheet of water in the Superior, Huron, and Michigan basins at this time is known as the Nipissing Great Lakes, and Leverett has suggested that this low level be called the North Bay stage.[1] The water dropped to below the present Lake Michigan level, and it is probable that the stage was of short duration.

ENGLEWOOD STAGE

Once again uplift in the northeast, consequent probably on further retreat of the ice, closed the lower outlet, and the level of the lake rose about 12 or 14 feet above the present surface, forming the Englewood stage. Drainage was both by way of the St. Clair River and the Chicago outlet, and the lakes at this stage are also known as the Nipissing Great Lakes. From Miller westward into Illinois the water near the shore must have been very shallow, for sand bars were formed in great abundance. These bars are best developed west of Gary, but are also seen in Chicago (Plate XX, *b*).

These off-shore bars form linear ridges with intervening swales which are in places filled with canal-like stretches of water. In height these bars range from 5 to 12 feet and they average 150 feet in width. The most remarkable feature is their extreme regularity, many extending for two or three miles with little change. Because of the industrial development around Hammond, Whiting, and Indiana Harbor, these ridges have been largely effaced in the western portion of Lake County, but in the region north of the Tolleston-Hammond beach there is an area about 4 miles

[1] Personal communication.

broad where they are the most conspicuous feature of the topography. The profile of the right of way of the Elgin, Joliet & Eastern Railway shows seventy of these ridges between the lake and the Tolleston-Hammond beach. From the lake to a point half a mile south of the Grand Calumet River the mean elevation of the surface is about 10 feet above the present lake, while the maximum and minimum figures are 17 and 3 feet, respectively. South of Fifth Avenue, Gary, the ridges are somewhat higher, the mean elevation above Lake Michigan being about 14 feet. On the Lake County map prepared by the Bureau of Soils these ridges are clearly indicated; and while different soil classifications are given in different areas, they appear to be the same physiographically.

These ridges presumably are former subaqueous bars, somewhat reworked by the wind. Such accumulations form in shallow water at the point where the wave breaks and material accumulates both from the landward shifting of sand by the wave and from the lakeward undertow. Such bars or barriers are very common in the shallow water just off the present shore; a series of at least three can usually be seen from good viewpoints on the dunes.[1] The upper portion of the ridges now on land is wind-blown, and a cross-section in Tolleston shows tangential bedding 5–6 feet below the original surface of the ridge. These ridges are roughly parallel with the shore and indicate filling at the head of the lake.

LAKE MICHIGAN

With continued adjustment of level to the north, the Strait of Mackinac and the St. Clair River came to their present elevation and the water surface dropped to that of the present Lake Michigan. Minor fluctuations in level, even to a few feet, are still found, due largely to winds and variations in barometric pressure. The following figures for the water-level of Lake Michigan are furnished by the United States Lake Survey:

	Feet
Mean stage, 1860–1918 (both inclusive)	581.16
High water, 1838	584.69
Lowest recorded monthly mean (December, 1895)	578.98
Standard low water	578.50

The original shore line of Lake Michigan was not the same as at present, for the changes now operative and previously described have built the beach lakeward in some areas and caused considerable encroachment by the lake in others.

[1] See D. W. Johnson, "Shore-Line Processes and Shore-Line Development" (1919), pp. 350–66, for detailed treatment.

How much dune accumulation has taken place along the eastern portion of the Indiana shore is unknown, for erosion is in progress and the dunes here are partially related to older shore lines. Since the Tolleston-Hammond beaches yielded a dune belt a quarter to half a mile wide, and since the duration of Lake Michigan has been much longer than any of these earlier stages, it seems probable that a dune belt at least as wide was built up by Lake Michigan. At Dune Park the dune belt of the present lake is half a mile wide, while at Miller the dunes of Lake Michigan proper are about a mile in width.

The cause of the change from deposition to erosion in the east is not clear, though presumably it was related to a change in the amount of sand supplied, and to some change in the lake currents. Such a change in the currents was doubtless a result of the winds which might naturally be expected to undergo slight changes with the disappearance of the ice sheet. Thus Lake Michigan is but a phase in the evolution of the basin, though it is by far the most important of the various lake stages here described.

RIVER DEVELOPMENT

Most of the streams of the area are sluggish and the lower portions of the land are therefore poorly drained. Deep River is the chief stream which has been eroding actively, and it flows in a rather narrow valley from 5 to 30 feet deep, cut in glacial till and lacustrine deposits. The greater depth of this valley has resulted from the greater height of the land which it drains.

Of the various streams, the Calumet River has had the most interesting history, its present course being largely the result of changes in the lake. During the Calumet stage this river cared for the drainage of the Chesterton embayment and emptied into the lake somewhere southeast of Dune Park. During the construction of the Tolleston beach this mouth was blocked by barrier beach accumulations. At that time, as now, beach sand was in transit to the west in this region, so that the mouth of the river was deflected progressively farther and farther west, until finally the Calumet River came to empty into the Sag outlet south of Blue Island. At this time the southward current along the west shore of the lake was drawn over into the Chicago outlet and so did not meet or check the current from the east shore at the head of the lake. The current from the east, therefore, continued as far as the Sag outlet. During the Englewood stage the Chicago outlet was less important, since drainage was partially to the north, and the southward current along the western shore of the lake continued to and beyond Miller. Thus the Calumet River was deflected back to the east again, emptying somewhere near Gary. Continued accumulation of sand on the western side of the stream mouth shifted the mouth of the river still farther to the east, the limit being reached about 1870, by which time the mouth of the Calumet was three-quarters of a mile beyond Miller, and was largely closed by the accumulation of sand. The War Department survey at this time shows less than a ten-foot contour interval between the river and the lake. Recently channels have been dug at Hegewisch and Indiana Harbor, so that the eastern portion of the Grand Calumet River has been reversed, and now empties through the above channels, which also care for the discharge of the Little Calumet River.

CHAPTER VI

BIBLIOGRAPHY

REFERENCES DEALING WITH THE AREA

A. GEOLOGICAL

W. C. ALDEN, "The Chicago Folio," *U.S. Geological Survey*, Folio No. 81 (1902).

EDMUND ANDREWS, "The North American Lakes Considered as Chronometers of Post-Glacial Time," *Trans. Chicago Academy of Science*, II (1870), 1–24.

——, "The Glacial Drift of Illinois," *American Journal of Science*, 3d series, XLIII (1867), 75–77.

WALLACE W. ATWOOD AND JAMES W. GOLDTHWAIT, "Physical Geology of the Evanston-Waukegan Region," *Illinois Geological Survey Bull.* 7 (1908).

E. STILLMAN BAILEY, "The Sand Dunes of Indiana." Chicago: McClurg & Co., 1927.

FRANK C. BAKER, "The Life of the Pleistocene," *University of Illinois Bulletin*, XVII (1920).

——, "The Life of Glacial Lake Chicago," *Science*, new series, XXXI (1910), 715–17.

W. S. BLATCHLEY, "The Geology of Lake and Porter Counties," *Indiana Department of Geology*, 22d Annual Report (1897), 25–184.

T. M. BUSHNELL AND WENDELL BARRETT, "Soil Survey of Lake County, Indiana," *U.S. Bureau of Soils*, Field Operations, 1917.

——, "Soil Survey of Porter County, Indiana," *U.S. Bureau of Soils*, Field Operations, 1916.

T. C. CHAMBERLIN, "Geology of Eastern Wisconsin," *Wisconsin Geological Survey*, II (1877), 230–32.

GEORGE B. CRESSEY, "Studies in the Sand Dunes of Northwestern Indiana." Chicago: University of Chicago, 1921.

——, "Notes on the Sand Dunes of Northwestern Indiana," *Journal of Geology*, XXX (1922), 248–51.

ELLIOT R. DOWNING, *A Naturalist in the Great Lakes Region*. Chicago: University of Chicago Press, 1922.

H. L. FAIRCHILD, "Musical Sands," *Science*, new series, LI (1920), 62.

E. O. FIRPIN, "Singing Sands," *Science*, new series, LI (1920), 64.

GEORGE D. FULLER, "Some Perched Dunes of Northern Lake Michigan," *Trans. Illinois Academy of Science*, IX (1918), 111–22.

JAMES W. GOLDTHWAIT, "The Abandoned Shore Lines of Eastern Wisconsin," *Wisconsin Geological and Natural History Survey Bull.* 17 (1907).

PETER S. GOODMAN, *The Indiana Sand Dunes* (map). Chicago: Rand McNally Co., 1920.

Mark W. Harrington, "Surface Currents of the Great Lakes," *U.S. Weather Bureau Bull. B* (1895).

A. F. Knotts, "The Dunes of Northwestern Indiana," *Indiana Department of Geology*, 41st Annual Report (1916), 11–27.

Frank Leverett, "Pleistocene Features and Deposits of the Chicago Area," *Chicago Academy of Science Bull. 2* (May, 1897).

——, "Wells of Indiana," *U.S. Geological Survey Water Supply Paper 21* (1899).

——, "The Illinois Glacial Lobe," *U.S. Geological Survey Monograph 38* (1899).

Frank Leverett and Frank Taylor, "The Pleistocene of Indiana and Michigan," *U.S. Geological Survey Monograph 53* (1915).

B. R. McKay, "Topographic Map of the Dune Park Region, with Explanation by R. D. Salisbury," *Geographic Society of Chicago* (1917).

Edward J. Quinn, "Soil Survey of La Porte County," *Indiana Department of Geology*, 36th Annual Report (1911), 281–89.

W. D. Richardson, "Singing Sands of Lake Michigan," *Science*, new series, L (1919), 493.

Rollin D. Salisbury and William C. Alden, "The Geography of Chicago and Its Environs," *Geographic Society of Chicago, Bull. 1*, revised ed., 1920.

Orpheus M. Schantz, "Indiana's Unrivalled Sand Dunes," *National Geographic Magazine*, XXXV (1919), 430–41.

Charles W. Shannon, "The Sand Areas of Indiana," *Proc. Indiana Academy of Science* (1911), 197–210.

Frank B. Taylor, "The Glacial and Post-Glacial Lakes of the Great Lakes Region," *Annual Report, Smithsonian Institute* (1912), 291–327.

Warren Upham, "Glacial Lake Nicolet," *American Geologist*, XXXII (1903), 105–15.

B. BOTANICAL AND POPULAR

George A. Brennan, *The Wonders of the Dunes*. Indianapolis: Bobbs Merrill Co., 1923.

H. C. Cowles, "The Ecological Relations of the Dune Flora," *Botanical Gazette*, XXVII (1899), 95–117, 167–202, 281–308, 361–91.

——, "The Plant Societies of Chicago and Vicinity," *Geographic Society of Chicago, Bull. 2* (1901).

Earl H. Reed, *The Dune Country*. New York: John Lane & Co., 1916.

——, *Voices of the Dunes*. Chicago: Aldebrink Press, 1912.

——, *Sketches in Duneland*. New York: John Lane & Co., 1918.

Stephen T. Mather, *The Proposed Sand Dunes National Park, Indiana*. Washington: Government Printing Office, 1917.

REFERENCES DEALING WITH THE PRINCIPLES INVOLVED

Hertha Ayrton, "The Origin and Growth of Ripple Mark," *Proc. Royal Society of London*, LXXXIV (1911), 285–310.

H. J. L. Beadnell, "Sand Dunes of the Libyan Desert," *Geographical Journal*, XXXV (1910), 379–95.

Walter H. Bucher, "The Origin of Ripples and Related Sedimentary Surface Forms," *American Journal of Science*, 3d series, XLVII (1919), 149–210.

Gerald O. Case, *Coast Sand Dunes*. London: St. Brides Press, 1914.

L. Cockayne, *The Dune Areas of New Zealand*. Wellington: Department of Lands, 1911.

Percy Collins, "Sand Devastation," *Scientific American Supplement*, LXXXIII (1917), 280–82.

Vaughn Cornish, "On the Formation of Sand Dunes," *Geographical Journal*, IX (1897), 278–309.

———, "Sea Beaches and Sea Banks," *Geographical Journal*, XI (1898), 520, 620.

———, "On Kumatology," *Geographical Journal*, XIII (1899), 624.

———, *Waves of Sand and Snow*. Chicago: Open Court Publishing Co., 1913.

C. L. Dake, "The Problem of the St. Peter Sandstone," *Missouri School of Mines Bulletin*, Vol. VI (1921).

E. E. Free, "The Movement of Soil Material by the Wind," *U.S. Bureau of Soils, Bull. 68* (1911).

J. J. Galloway, "On the Rounding of Sand Grains by Solution," *American Journal of Science*, 3d series, XLVII (1919), 270–80.

———, "The Value of the Physical Characters of Sand Grains in the Interpretation of the Origin of Sandstones," *Bull. Geological Society of America*, XXXIII (1922), 104.

M. I. Goldman, "Petrography and Genesis of the Upper Cretaceous of Maryland," *Maryland Geological Survey*, "Upper Cretaceous" (1916), 111–282.

———, "The Catahoula Sandstone of Texas," *American Journal of Science*, 3d series, XXXIX (1915), 261–87.

J. G. Goodchild, "Desert Conditions in Britain," *Trans. Edinburgh Geological Society*, VII (1890), 203–22.

A. W. Grabau, *Principles of Stratigraphy* (New York: A. G. Seiler & Co., 1913), 52–61, 253–56, 286–89, 549–65.

Edouard Harle and Jacques Harle, "Memoirs sur Les Dunes de Gascogne," *Bulletin de la Section de Geographie* (Paris, 1919).

C. A. Hart and H. A. Gleason, "On the Biology of the Sand Areas of Illinois," *Bull. Illinois State Laboratory of Natural History*, VII (1910), 137–272.

Sven Hedin, *Scientific Results of a Journey in Central Asia*. Vols. I and II. Stockholm: Lithographic Institute, 1904.

L. L. Hopkins, *Sand: Its Occurrence, Properties, and Uses: A Bibliography*. Pittsburgh: Carnegie Library, 1918.

Douglas W. Johnson, "Shore-Line Processes and Shore-Line Development." New York: John Wiley & Sons, 1919.

E. M. Kindle, "Recent and Fossil Ripple Marks," *Canadian Geological Survey, Museum Bulletin 25*, (1917).

W. J. HARDING KING, "The Nature and Formation of Ripples and Dunes," *Geographical Journal*, XLVII (1916), 189–297.

WILLIAM MACKIE, "On the Laws that Govern the Rounding of a Particle of Sand," *Trans. Edinburgh Geological Society*, VII (1899), 298–311.

PEHR OLSSON-SEFFER, "The Relation of the Wind to the Topography of Coastal Drift Sands," *Journal of Geology*, XVI (1908), 549–64.

———, "The Genesis and Development of Sand Formations on Marine Coasts," *Augustana Library Publication No. 7* (Rock Island, Illinois, 1910)·

N. S. SHALER, "The Phenomena of Beach and Dune Sands," *Bull. Geological Society of America*, V (1894), 207–12.

W. H. SHERZER, "Criteria for the Recognition of Various Types of Sand Grains," *Bull. Geological Society of America*, XXI (1909), 625–62.

N. A. SOKOLOW, *Die Dunen.* Berlin: Julius Springer, 1894.

JOHN A. UDDEN, "The Mechanical Composition of Wind Deposits," *Augustana Library Publication No. 1* (Rock Island, Illinois, 1898).

———, "Mechanical Composition of Clastic Sediments," *Bull. Geological Society of America*, XXV (1913), 655–744.

CHESTER K. WENTWORTH, "A Scale of Grade and Size for Clastic Sediments," *Journal of Geology*, XXX (1922), 377–92.

C. CARUS WILSON, "Musical Sand," *Trans. Bournemouth Society of Natural History* (November, 1888).

VICTOR ZEIGLER, "Factors Influencing the Rounding of Sand Grains," *Journal of Geology*, XIX (1911), 645–54.

PLATE II

The main dune complex, looking east from Mount Tom, north of Tremont. From photograph by A. E. Ormes.

PLATE III

a, Side view of blowout dune at Waverly Beach. From photograph by Frances La Follette.

b, Long Lake, looking east. The dunes to the north belong to Lake Michigan, while the Tolleston Beach is to the south. From photograph by Frances La Follette.

PLATE IV

a, Beach cusps

b, The beach at Miller. From photograph by H. N. Mudge

PLATE V

a, Erosion along the western shore of Lake Michigan, near Ravinia. The beach is widened in the foreground because of a breakwater from which the photograph was taken.

b, Erosional face of the dunes north of Port Chester. From photograph by F. H. Culver.

PLATE VI

a, The main dune complex looking north from Calumet Beach at Tremont. Mounts Tom, Holden, and Green in the background.

b, Erosion along the eastern shore of Lake Michigan. The upper part of the sand is wet and so does not lie at the angle of rest.

PLATE VII

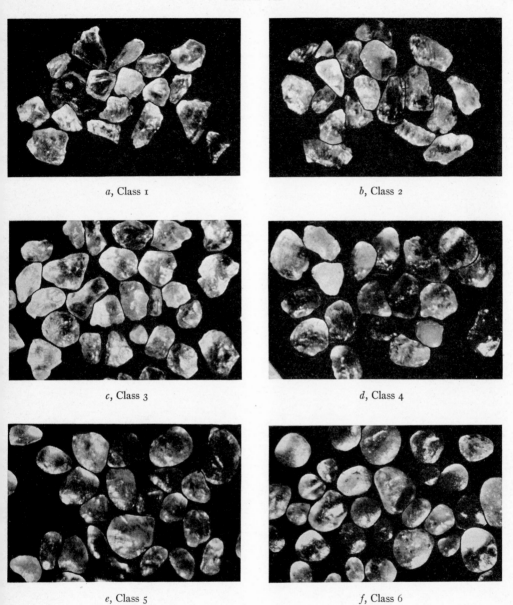

a, Class 1

b, Class 2

c, Class 3

d, Class 4

e, Class 5

f, Class 6

Stages in the rounding of sand grains. Scale ×24

PLATE VIII

a, Common ripples, all of the grains being approximately the same size. From photograph by H. N. Mudge.

b, Ripples with coarser grains comprising the crests

PLATE IX

a, Turret dunes, north of Port Chester. Mount Tom in the distance. From photograph by A. W. Strickler.

b, Lee dunes

PLATE X

a, Accumulation of sand around an open fence, near Michigan City

b, Eolian stratification, Dune Park. From photograph by E. S. Bastin

PLATE XI

a, Tangential cross-bedding typical of windblown deposits

b, The beginning of a new fore dune ridge in front of a more fully developed fore dune, west of Miller Beach. From photograph by G. D. Fuller.

PLATE XII

Fore dune ridges within the main dune complex. From photograph by A. E. Ormes

PLATE XIII

a, Developing fore dune due to the widening of the beach near a breakwater, east of Michigan City. A second and earlier fore dune ridge is present between the shore and the high dunes.

b, A small blowout, north of Port Chester

PLATE XIV

a, The beginning of a blowout along an erosional shore. From photograph by H. N. Mudge.

b, A fully developed blowout, north of Port Chester. From photograph by F. H. Culver.

PLATE XV

a, A fore dune ridge built across the mouth of a mature blowout, north of Wicliffe. From photograph by A. E. Ormes.

b, A small blowout dune filling up a larger blowout, north of Furnessville. This represents the next stage beyond Figure *a* on this plate. From photograph by Frances La Follette.

PLATE XVI

a, A small dune migrating into a blowout. From photograph by P. T. Tarnoski

b, A blowout beginning to be stablized by vegetation. A fore dune is being built along the shore. From photograph by H. N. Mudge.

PLATE XVII

a, Crescentic dune, Dune Park. From photograph by Frances La Follette

b, Lee slope of blowout dune, north of Furnessville. From photograph by A. E. Ormes.

PLATE XVIII

a, Slumping sand as typically developed after a rain. From photograph by Roy Flowers.

b, Dune sand, showing lee stratification, above horizontally bedded lake sand

PLATE XIX

a, Eolian cross-bedded sand overlying clay, west of Michigan City

b, Exposure of sand and clay, along Johnsfield Creek

PLATE XX

a, The meadow-like marsh between the main dune complex and the Calumet Beach. Tamarack swamp in the center distance. Looking east from north of Oak Hill. From photograph by F. H. Culver.

b, Linear beach ridges, west of Clark Road

INDEX